Facts at Your Fingertips 2
Rapid Recall Strategies for 'Times-Tables' Facts
A Photocopiable Activity Book by:
Helen Maden

C000271931

Introduction

The four rules of number are the foundation of numeracy work in the Primary School. Curriculum 2000 for Mathematics details how emphasis should be placed on developing the knowledge and understanding of mental calculations, then progressing to more formal written calculations.

The National Numeracy Framework for teaching mathematics outlines how recall of multiplication and division facts should first be taught through strategies so that children fully understand their methods rather than carrying them out 'by rote'.

This book is suitable for children in upper KS1 and lower KS2 who are learning their tables and division facts and for children in upper KS2 who are consolidating this knowledge and understanding. The exercises will take your children 'Step by Step' through a tried and tested system which teaches multiplication and division recall so that children have tables facts 'at their fingertips'.

Other books in this series include:
Facts at Your Fingertips 1 (for addition and subtraction within 20)
Addition and Subtraction (using Expanded Written Methods)
Multiplication and Division (using Expanded Written Methods)
Addition and Subtraction 4 Rules of Number (for compact calculation practice)

Topical Resources publishes a range of Educational Materials for use in Primary Schools and Pre-School Nurseries and Playgroups.

For latest catalogue:
Tel: 01772 863158
Fax: 01772 866153

E.Mail: sales@topical-resources.co.uk
Visit our Website: www.topical-resources.co.uk

Printed in Great Britain for 'Topical Resources', Publishers of Educational Materials, P.O. Box 329, Broughton, Preston, PR3 5LT by T.Snape & Company Ltd, Boltons Court, Preston, England.

Typeset by Paul Sealey Illustration and Design, 3 Wentworth Drive, Thornton, England. FY5 5AR.

First Published April 2004
ISBN 1 872977 86 3

Contents

Methodology

The learning of 'times tables' and the quick recall of such facts are central to understanding and carrying out more difficult mathematical problems.

Children generally find the 6x, 7x and 8x tables the most difficult to master. In this tried and tested method, instead of learning 'times tables' in the traditional order (i.e. 2x, 5x, 10x, 3x, 4x, 6x, 7x, 8x, 9x), the facts are learnt in the following order:

1x, 0x, 10x, 2x, 5x, Squares, 9x.

(Squares = 0x0, 1x1, 2x2, 3x3, 4x4, 5x5, 6x6, 7x7, 8x8, 9x9, 10 x 10)

Once children have mastered these 'easy' tables and they understand that multiplication is commutative (i.e. 3x10 gives the same answer as 10x3), there are just 10 remaining facts to remember:

Four facts from the 3x table: **3x4, 3x6, 3x7, 3x8,**
Three facts from the 4x table: **4x6, 4x7, 4x8,**
Only **two** facts from the 6x table: **6x7, 6x8**
And **only** one fact from the 8x table: **7x8**

After teaching the above tables in the given order (plus the 10 remaining facts), children will become faster at recalling multiplication and division facts by regularly using the following worksheets in timed situations. The pages can be used as a whole sheet or cut into strips if fewer questions are required. The sheets may also be used for homework as this will provide additional reinforcement and consolidation of the children's knowledge and understanding. Once the children are confident with a particular strategy, we have found that they enjoy being timed and subsequently, set targets for improvement for themselves.

There is a photocopiable certificate on the last page that can be used when a child successfully masters any strategy. E.g. **'I now know how to multiply by 10'**

Multiplication Square

	0	1	2	3	4	5	6	7	8	9	10
0	0	0	0	0	0	0	0	0	0	0	0
1	0	1	2	3	4	5	6	7	8	9	10
2	0	2	4	6	8	10	12	14	16	18	20
3	0	3	6	9	**12**	15	**18**	**21**	**24**	27	30
4	0	4	8	**12**	16	20	**24**	**28**	**32**	36	40
5	0	5	10	15	20	25	30	35	40	45	50
6	0	6	12	**18**	**24**	30	36	**42**	**48**	54	60
7	0	7	14	**21**	**28**	35	**42**	49	**56**	63	70
8	0	8	16	**24**	**32**	40	**48**	**56**	64	72	80
9	0	9	18	27	36	45	54	63	72	81	90
10	0	10	20	30	40	50	60	70	80	90	100

Order to learn tables:

Strategy A	1 times
Strategy B	0 times
Strategy C	10 times
Strategy D	2 times
Strategy E	5 times
Strategy F	Squares
Strategy G	9 times
Strategy H	Others (i.e. the 10 remaining facts)

The 10 facts left to learn

3x4=12	4x6= 24	6x7= 42	7x8= 56
3x6=18	4x7= 28	6x8= 48	
3x7=21	4x8= 32		
3x8=24			

Teachers' Notes - Multiplication Facts Diagnostic Test

A simple diagnostic test has been provided for use before the various worksheets. The test clearly shows how the exercises develop and where they can be found in the book. The questions below should be read out and the children individually write down the answers.

1   It should be explained to the children that the easiest facts are at the top of each column and the facts at the bottom of each column may be more difficult so they should not worry or linger over a fact if they cannot remember them.

2   Children should be told to put a line (e.g. ━) if they are unsure of the answer, as this will help them progress to the next question rather than get behind.

3   The teacher should read the questions quite quickly as this test is to assess instant recall rather than testing whether children can 'work out' the multiplication facts.

Questions to be read aloud by teacher

1 1 x 4 =	**12** 7 x 0 =	**23** 9 x 1 =	**34** 0 x 4 =
2 10 x 5 =	**13** 6 x 10 =	**24** 10 x 4 =	**35** 3 x 10 =
3 6 x 2 =	**14** 8 x 2 =	**25** 7 x 2 =	**36** 9 x 2 =
4 4 x 5 =	**15** 5 x 5 =	**26** 9 x 5 =	**37** 7 x 5 =
5 9 x 9 =	**16** 7 x 7 =	**27** 6 x 6 =	**38** 8 x 8 =
6 3 x 3 =	**17** 4 x 4 =	**28** 5 x 5 =	**39** 10 x 10 =
7 3 x 9 =	**18** 7 x 9 =	**29** 9 x 5 =	**40** 9 x 4 =
8 6 x 9 =	**19** 8 x 9 =	**30** 9 x 9 =	**41** 6 x 9 =
9 3 x 7 =	**20** 3 x 8 =	**31** 3 x 6 =	**42** 3 x 4 =
10 4 x 3 =	**21** 4 x 6 =	**32** 4 x 7 =	**43** 4 x 8 =
11 6 x 7 =	**22** 6 x 8 =	**33** 7 x 8 =	**44** 8 x 6 =

Pupil's Answer Sheet

Children should write their answers in the spaces provided. Ticks and crosses should be used to mark the work. Four crosses in a line e.g. Qu 5, *16, 27 & 38* would show more work required on Strategy F: Squares.

- -

Multiplication Assessment Sheet (Recall of Facts)

Name —————————————————————   Date ———————————————

				Table(s) Tested	Exercises to go to if any facts incorrect
1	**12**	**23**	**34**	x1 and x0	18
2	**13**	**24**	**35**	x10	1, 19, 35
3	**14**	**25**	**36**	x2	2, 11, 20, 28, 36
4	**15**	**26**	**37**	x5	3, 12, 13, 21, 29, 30, 37
5	**16**	**27**	**38**	Squares	4, 22, 38
6	**17**	**28**	**39**	Squares	4, 22, 38
7	**18**	**29**	**40**	x9	5, 14, 23, 31, 39
8	**19**	**30**	**41**	x9	5, 14, 23, 31, 39
9	**20**	**31**	**42**	x3	6, 24, 40
10	**21**	**32**	**43**	x4	7, 15, 25, 32, 41
11	**22**	**33**	**44**	x6, x7, x8	8, 9, 10, 16, 17, 26, 33, 34, 42, 43, 44

Exercise 1A	Exercise 1B	Exercise 1C	Exercise 1D
Name:	Name:	Name:	Name:
Date:	Date:	Date:	Date:

1 $10 \times 7 =$	**26** $0 \times 10 =$	**51** $9 \times 10 =$	**76** $7 \times 10 =$
2 $9 \times 10 =$	**27** $10 \times 7 =$	**52** $10 \times 3 =$	**77** $10 \times 4 =$
3 $0 \times 10 =$	**28** $3 \times 10 =$	**53** $2 \times 10 =$	**78** $9 \times 10 =$
4 $10 \times 5 =$	**29** $10 \times 2 =$	**54** $10 \times 8 =$	**79** $10 \times 3 =$
5 $10 \times 10 =$	**30** $4 \times 10 =$	**55** $1 \times 10 =$	**80** $6 \times 10 =$
6 $6 \times 10 =$	**31** $10 \times 1 =$	**56** $4 \times 10 =$	**81** $10 \times 7 =$
7 $10 \times 1 =$	**32** $6 \times 10 =$	**57** $7 \times 10 =$	**82** $5 \times 10 =$
8 $1 \times 10 =$	**33** $9 \times 10 =$	**58** $10 \times 0 =$	**83** $1 \times 10 =$
9 $10 \times 8 =$	**34** $10 \times 4 =$	**59** $2 \times 10 =$	**84** $10 \times 5 =$
10 $3 \times 10 =$	**35** $8 \times 10 =$	**60** $10 \times 7 =$	**85** $2 \times 10 =$
11 $10 \times 2 =$	**36** $10 \times 7 =$	**61** $10 \times 10 =$	**86** $8 \times 10 =$
12 $10 \times 4 =$	**37** $5 \times 10 =$	**62** $10 \times 3 =$	**87** $10 \times 6 =$
13 $7 \times 10 =$	**38** $10 \times 8 =$	**63** $6 \times 10 =$	**88** $9 \times 10 =$
14 $2 \times 10 =$	**39** $4 \times 10 =$	**64** $4 \times 10 =$	**89** $10 \times 10 =$
15 $10 \times 8 =$	**40** $3 \times 10 =$	**65** $10 \times 5 =$	**90** $10 \times 1 =$
16 $3 \times 10 =$	**41** $10 \times 6 =$	**66** $6 \times 10 =$	**91** $8 \times 10 =$
17 $10 \times 4 =$	**42** $5 \times 10 =$	**67** $10 \times 1 =$	**92** $10 \times 3 =$
18 $7 \times 10 =$	**43** $10 \times 9 =$	**68** $4 \times 10 =$	**93** $2 \times 10 =$
19 $10 \times 0 =$	**44** $7 \times 10 =$	**69** $5 \times 10 =$	**94** $10 \times 9 =$
20 $1 \times 10 =$	**45** $10 \times 2 =$	**70** $10 \times 10 =$	**95** $2 \times 10 =$
21 $5 \times 10 =$	**46** $1 \times 10 =$	**71** $10 \times 5 =$	**96** $4 \times 10 =$
22 $10 \times 10 =$	**47** $10 \times 10 =$	**72** $8 \times 10 =$	**97** $10 \times 3 =$
23 $9 \times 10 =$	**48** $10 \times 0 =$	**73** $10 \times 6 =$	**98** $10 \times 10 =$
24 $10 \times 6 =$	**49** $9 \times 10 =$	**74** $9 \times 10 =$	**99** $10 \times 1 =$
25 $2 \times 10 =$	**50** $10 \times 1 =$	**75** $10 \times 7 =$	**100** $4 \times 10 =$

Time?	Time?	Time?	Time?
How did you do?	Have you reached your target?	Try to be faster?	What is your time?

Exercise 2A	Exercise 2B	Exercise 2C	Exercise 2D
Name:	Name:	Name:	Name:
Date:	Date:	Date:	Date:

1 1 x 2 =	26 2 x 2 =	51 3 x 2 =	76 10 x 2 =
2 2 x 3 =	27 2 x 1 =	52 2 x 6 =	77 2 x 9 =
3 10 x 2 =	28 5 x 2 =	53 7 x 2 =	78 1 x 2 =
4 2 x 2 =	29 2 x 1 =	54 2 x 9 =	79 2 x 7 =
5 2 x 1 =	30 2 x 2 =	55 6 x 2 =	80 2 x 9 =
6 9 x 2 =	31 8 x 2 =	56 2 x 7 =	81 2 x 2 =
7 2 x 4 =	32 2 x 3 =	57 2 x 2 =	82 2 x 1 =
8 2 x 2 =	33 1 x 2 =	58 2 x 5 =	83 9 x 2 =
9 1 x 2 =	34 2 x 4 =	59 8 x 2 =	84 2 x 3 =
10 3 x 2 =	35 10 x 2 =	60 2 x 1 =	85 8 x 2 =
11 2 x 7 =	36 9 x 2 =	61 8 x 2 =	86 2 x 2 =
12 2 x 2 =	37 2 x 9 =	62 2 x 9 =	87 6 x 2 =
13 2 x 4 =	38 3 x 2 =	63 4 x 2 =	88 4 x 2 =
14 5 x 2 =	39 2 x 6 =	64 2 x 10 =	89 2 x 6 =
15 2 x 3 =	40 4 x 2 =	65 10 x 2 =	90 3 x 2 =
16 2 x 6 =	41 2 x 8 =	66 4 x 2 =	91 2 x 5 =
17 4 x 2 =	42 2 x 2 =	67 2 x 6 =	92 7 x 2 =
18 7 x 2 =	43 2 x 5 =	68 3 x 2 =	93 2 x 4 =
19 2 x 10 =	44 10 x 2 =	69 2 x 1 =	94 8 x 2 =
20 5 x 2 =	45 2 x 7 =	70 7 x 2 =	95 2 x 6 =
21 2 x 6 =	46 3 x 2 =	71 5 x 2 =	96 10 x 2 =
22 8 x 2 =	47 2 x 6 =	72 2 x 1 =	97 5 x 2 =
23 2 x 7 =	48 4 x 2 =	73 2 x 2 =	98 2 x 7 =
24 5 x 2 =	49 2 x 9 =	74 2 x 8 =	99 1 x 2 =
25 2 x 8 =	50 7 x 2 =	75 2 x 2 =	100 2 x 8 =

Time?	Time?	Time?	Time?

Did you beat your score?

Is this your best score yet?

Try to be even quicker next time!

Did you use any strategies?

Exercise 3A	Exercise 3B	Exercise 3C	Exercise 3D
Name:	Name:	Name:	Name:
Date:	Date:	Date:	Date:
1. $5 \times 1 =$	26. $1 \times 5 =$	51. $1 \times 5 =$	76. $5 \times 5 =$
2. $4 \times 5 =$	27. $5 \times 4 =$	52. $5 \times 9 =$	77. $7 \times 5 =$
3. $5 \times 7 =$	28. $7 \times 5 =$	53. $5 \times 5 =$	78. $5 \times 4 =$
4. $5 \times 2 =$	29. $5 \times 2 =$	54. $10 \times 5 =$	79. $2 \times 5 =$
5. $8 \times 5 =$	30. $5 \times 1 =$	55. $5 \times 2 =$	80. $5 \times 6 =$
6. $5 \times 5 =$	31. $3 \times 5 =$	56. $8 \times 5 =$	81. $3 \times 5 =$
7. $3 \times 5 =$	32. $6 \times 5 =$	57. $5 \times 6 =$	82. $5 \times 1 =$
8. $9 \times 5 =$	33. $5 \times 4 =$	58. $7 \times 5 =$	83. $5 \times 8 =$
9. $5 \times 4 =$	34. $2 \times 5 =$	59. $5 \times 3 =$	84. $2 \times 5 =$
10. $6 \times 5 =$	35. $5 \times 3 =$	60. $7 \times 5 =$	85. $9 \times 5 =$
11. $9 \times 5 =$	36. $8 \times 5 =$	61. $5 \times 2 =$	86. $2 \times 5 =$
12. $5 \times 5 =$	37. $5 \times 5 =$	62. $4 \times 5 =$	87. $5 \times 1 =$
13. $3 \times 5 =$	38. $10 \times 5 =$	63. $3 \times 5 =$	88. $3 \times 5 =$
14. $1 \times 5 =$	39. $5 \times 3 =$	64. $5 \times 8 =$	89. $5 \times 3 =$
15. $5 \times 6 =$	40. $6 \times 5 =$	65. $6 \times 5 =$	90. $10 \times 5 =$
16. $4 \times 5 =$	41. $2 \times 5 =$	66. $5 \times 5 =$	91. $5 \times 7 =$
17. $5 \times 2 =$	42. $5 \times 7 =$	67. $3 \times 5 =$	92. $4 \times 5 =$
18. $7 \times 5 =$	43. $8 \times 5 =$	68. $5 \times 9 =$	93. $5 \times 9 =$
19. $5 \times 3 =$	44. $5 \times 5 =$	69. $4 \times 5 =$	94. $6 \times 5 =$
20. $8 \times 5 =$	45. $8 \times 5 =$	70. $6 \times 5 =$	95. $5 \times 5 =$
21. $5 \times 9 =$	46. $6 \times 5 =$	71. $5 \times 4 =$	96. $8 \times 5 =$
22. $2 \times 5 =$	47. $5 \times 9 =$	72. $10 \times 5 =$	97. $4 \times 5 =$
23. $10 \times 5 =$	48. $1 \times 5 =$	73. $5 \times 7 =$	98. $5 \times 6 =$
24. $5 \times 0 =$	49. $10 \times 5 =$	74. $2 \times 5 =$	99. $8 \times 5 =$
25. $1 \times 5 =$	50. $5 \times 7 =$	75. $5 \times 1 =$	100. $7 \times 5 =$
Time?	Time?	Time?	Time?
Which facts did you find the hardest?	Did you beat your target?	Can you try to be faster?	Where do you need to improve?

Exercise 4A	Exercise 4B	Exercise 4C	Exercise 4D
Name:	Name:	Name:	Name:
Date:	Date:	Date:	Date:

	Exercise 4A		Exercise 4B		Exercise 4C		Exercise 4D
1	1 x 1 =	**26**	9 x 9 =	**51**	7 x 7 =	**76**	4 x 4 =
2	8 x 8 =	**27**	4 x 4 =	**52**	2 x 2 =	**77**	10 x 10 =
3	9 x 9 =	**28**	1 x 1 =	**53**	9 x 9 =	**78**	6 x 6 =
4	2 x 2 =	**29**	8 x 8 =	**54**	4 x 4 =	**79**	3 x 3 =
5	7 x 7 =	**30**	3 x 3 =	**55**	10 x 10 =	**80**	8 x 8 =
6	2 x 2 =	**31**	10 x 10 =	**56**	6 x 6 =	**81**	9 x 9 =
7	9 x 9 =	**32**	5 x 5 =	**57**	3 x 3 =	**82**	2 x 2 =
8	4 x 4 =	**33**	1 x 1 =	**58**	10 x 10 =	**83**	7 x 7 =
9	10 x 10 =	**34**	4 x 4 =	**59**	5 x 5 =	**84**	9 x 9 =
10	6 x 6 =	**35**	6 x 6 =	**60**	8 x 8 =	**85**	4 x 4 =
11	3 x 3 =	**36**	3 x 3 =	**61**	9 x 9 =	**86**	10 x 10 =
12	10 x 10 =	**37**	7 x 7 =	**62**	2 x 2 =	**87**	6 x 6 =
13	5 x 5 =	**38**	2 x 2 =	**63**	7 x 7 =	**88**	3 x 3 =
14	1 x 1 =	**39**	9 x 9 =	**64**	9 x 9 =	**89**	5 x 5 =
15	4 x 4 =	**40**	4 x 4 =	**65**	4 x 4 =	**90**	1 x 1 =
16	1 x 1 =	**41**	10 x 10 =	**66**	10 x 10 =	**91**	4 x 4 =
17	6 x 6 =	**42**	6 x 6 =	**67**	6 x 6 =	**92**	6 x 6 =
18	3 x 3 =	**43**	3 x 3 =	**68**	3 x 3 =	**93**	3 x 3 =
19	5 x 5 =	**44**	5 x 5 =	**69**	5 x 5 =	**94**	5 x 5 =
20	2 x 2 =	**45**	10 x 10 =	**70**	1 x 1 =	**95**	2 x 2 =
21	7 x 7 =	**46**	6 x 6 =	**71**	4 x 4 =	**96**	7 x 7 =
22	6 x 6 =	**47**	3 x 3 =	**72**	6 x 6 =	**97**	6 x 6 =
23	3 x 3 =	**48**	1 x 1 =	**73**	3 x 3 =	**98**	3 x 3 =
24	8 x 8 =	**49**	4 x 4 =	**74**	5 x 5 =	**99**	9 x 9 =
25	7 x 7 =	**50**	8 x 8 =	**75**	2 x 2 =	**100**	8 x 8 =

Time?	Time?	Time?	Time?

Is this your best score?

Have you reached your target?

Did you do well?

Do you think you are improving?

Exercise 5A	Exercise 5B	Exercise 5C	Exercise 5D
Name:	Name:	Name:	Name:
Date:	Date:	Date:	Date:

Exercise 5A	Exercise 5B	Exercise 5C	Exercise 5D
1 $0 \times 9 =$	**26** $9 \times 7 =$	**51** $9 \times 1 =$	**76** $2 \times 9 =$
2 $9 \times 2 =$	**27** $3 \times 9 =$	**52** $8 \times 9 =$	**77** $9 \times 1 =$
3 $4 \times 9 =$	**28** $9 \times 10 =$	**53** $9 \times 5 =$	**78** $7 \times 9 =$
4 $1 \times 9 =$	**29** $6 \times 9 =$	**54** $0 \times 9 =$	**79** $0 \times 9 =$
5 $9 \times 7 =$	**30** $9 \times 1 =$	**55** $7 \times 9 =$	**80** $9 \times 1 =$
6 $7 \times 9 =$	**31** $4 \times 9 =$	**56** $9 \times 9 =$	**81** $9 \times 9 =$
7 $9 \times 2 =$	**32** $9 \times 5 =$	**57** $2 \times 9 =$	**82** $9 \times 6 =$
8 $8 \times 9 =$	**33** $2 \times 9 =$	**58** $9 \times 4 =$	**83** $0 \times 9 =$
9 $1 \times 9 =$	**34** $9 \times 9 =$	**59** $6 \times 9 =$	**84** $9 \times 7 =$
10 $9 \times 3 =$	**35** $4 \times 9 =$	**60** $9 \times 3 =$	**85** $10 \times 9 =$
11 $0 \times 9 =$	**36** $9 \times 9 =$	**61** $10 \times 9 =$	**86** $9 \times 3 =$
12 $9 \times 2 =$	**37** $6 \times 9 =$	**62** $9 \times 2 =$	**87** $8 \times 9 =$
13 $9 \times 9 =$	**38** $9 \times 3 =$	**63** $9 \times 9 =$	**88** $4 \times 9 =$
14 $4 \times 9 =$	**39** $5 \times 9 =$	**64** $9 \times 4 =$	**89** $9 \times 4 =$
15 $9 \times 10 =$	**40** $9 \times 8 =$	**65** $3 \times 9 =$	**90** $1 \times 9 =$
16 $3 \times 9 =$	**41** $2 \times 9 =$	**66** $9 \times 8 =$	**91** $9 \times 8 =$
17 $5 \times 9 =$	**42** $6 \times 9 =$	**67** $5 \times 9 =$	**92** $5 \times 9 =$
18 $9 \times 6 =$	**43** $9 \times 1 =$	**68** $9 \times 1 =$	**93** $9 \times 2 =$
19 $9 \times 9 =$	**44** $7 \times 9 =$	**69** $4 \times 9 =$	**94** $9 \times 9 =$
20 $9 \times 6 =$	**45** $9 \times 2 =$	**70** $2 \times 9 =$	**95** $6 \times 9 =$
21 $9 \times 1 =$	**46** $0 \times 9 =$	**71** $9 \times 6 =$	**96** $9 \times 4 =$
22 $5 \times 9 =$	**47** $9 \times 7 =$	**72** $5 \times 9 =$	**97** $9 \times 9 =$
23 $9 \times 7 =$	**48** $10 \times 9 =$	**73** $9 \times 1 =$	**98** $9 \times 7 =$
24 $10 \times 9 =$	**49** $9 \times 8 =$	**74** $7 \times 9 =$	**99** $3 \times 9 =$
25 $9 \times 8 =$	**50** $1 \times 9 =$	**75** $9 \times 3 =$	**100** $9 \times 8 =$

Time?	Time?	Time?	Time?
Try to concentrate even more!	How do you think you are doing?	What have you learnt today?	How could you recall these facts even quicker

Exercise 6A	Exercise 6B	Exercise 6C	Exercise 6D
Name:	Name:	Name:	Name:
Date:	Date:	Date:	Date:

1 7 x 3 =	**26** 4 x 3 =	**51** 1 x 3 =	**76** 3 x 3 =
2 3 x 4 =	**27** 3 x 1 =	**52** 3 x 8 =	**77** 3 x 9 =
3 8 x 3 =	**28** 10 x 3 =	**53** 5 x 3 =	**78** 10 x 3 =
4 3 x 5 =	**29** 3 x 5 =	**54** 3 x 2 =	**79** 3 x 2 =
5 3 x 8 =	**30** 3 x 7 =	**55** 7 x 3 =	**80** 8 x 3 =
6 2 x 3 =	**31** 2 x 3 =	**56** 3 x 4 =	**81** 2 x 3 =
7 3 x 1 =	**32** 3 x 1 =	**57** 6 x 3 =	**82** 3 x 1 =
8 9 x 3 =	**33** 6 x 3 =	**58** 3 x 3 =	**83** 10 x 3 =
9 3 x 6 =	**34** 9 x 3 =	**59** 3 x 1 =	**84** 3 x 4 =
10 10 x 3 =	**35** 3 x 3 =	**60** 9 x 3 =	**85** 7 x 3 =
11 2 x 3 =	**36** 10 x 3 =	**61** 3 x 7 =	**86** 3 x 6 =
12 3 x 10 =	**37** 3 x 1 =	**62** 4 x 3 =	**87** 2 x 3 =
13 7 x 3 =	**38** 4 x 3 =	**63** 6 x 3 =	**88** 3 x 1 =
14 3 x 4 =	**39** 3 x 7 =	**64** 3 x 10 =	**89** 9 x 3 =
15 1 x 3 =	**40** 2 x 3 =	**65** 8 x 3 =	**90** 4 x 3 =
16 3 x 3 =	**41** 3 x 5 =	**66** 3 x 5 =	**91** 3 x 6 =
17 3 x 8 =	**42** 9 x 3 =	**67** 3 x 3 =	**92** 2 x 3 =
18 2 x 3 =	**43** 3 x 2 =	**68** 3 x 10 =	**93** 3 x 8 =
19 3 x 10 =	**44** 3 x 8 =	**69** 1 x 3 =	**94** 3 x 3 =
20 4 x 3 =	**45** 6 x 3 =	**70** 3 x 6 =	**95** 5 x 3 =
21 9 x 3 =	**46** 3 x 4 =	**71** 3 x 2 =	**96** 3 x 4 =
22 3 x 5 =	**47** 3 x 3 =	**72** 9 x 3 =	**97** 3 x 3 =
23 1 x 3 =	**48** 3 x 7 =	**73** 4 x 3 =	**98** 9 x 3 =
24 3 x 3 =	**49** 9 x 3 =	**74** 3 x 1 =	**99** 3 x 7 =
25 3 x 6 =	**50** 3 x 8 =	**75** 7 x 3 =	**100** 5 x 3 =

Time?	Time?	Time?	Time?

Are the facts at your fingertips?	Try to really focus!	Which facts do you find the easiest?	Did you do well?

Exercise 7A	Exercise 7B	Exercise 7C	Exercise 7D
Name:	Name:	Name:	Name:
Date:	Date:	Date:	Date:

#	7A	#	7B	#	7C	#	7D
1	1 x 4 =	26	4 x 0 =	51	4 x 8 =	76	4 x 0 =
2	4 x 0 =	27	2 x 4 =	52	2 x 4 =	77	3 x 4 =
3	5 x 4 =	28	6 x 4 =	53	5 x 4 =	78	4 x 1 =
4	2 x 4 =	29	4 x 9 =	54	4 x 0 =	79	4 x 4 =
5	4 x 7 =	30	4 x 4 =	55	9 x 4 =	80	4 x 0 =
6	4 x 4 =	31	8 x 4 =	56	4 x 3 =	81	6 x 4 =
7	9 x 4 =	32	4 x 2 =	57	4 x 4 =	82	4 x 2 =
8	4 x 6 =	33	0 x 4 =	58	4 x 6 =	83	8 x 4 =
9	0 x 4 =	34	4 x 5 =	59	2 x 4 =	84	4 x 10 =
10	4 x 4 =	35	10 x 4 =	60	4 x 9 =	85	7 x 4 =
11	10 x 4 =	36	4 x 7 =	61	0 x 4 =	86	4 x 4 =
12	8 x 4 =	37	2 x 4 =	62	8 x 4 =	87	1 x 4 =
13	4 x 5 =	38	8 x 4 =	63	4 x 5 =	88	5 x 4 =
14	6 x 4 =	39	4 x 4 =	64	10 x 4 =	89	9 x 4 =
15	4 x 1 =	40	6 x 4 =	65	4 x 4 =	90	4 x 2 =
16	9 x 4 =	41	4 x 3 =	66	3 x 4 =	91	3 x 4 =
17	4 x 3 =	42	7 x 4 =	67	4 x 7 =	92	4 x 1 =
18	6 x 4 =	43	4 x 1 =	68	2 x 4 =	93	7 x 4 =
19	4 x 8 =	44	9 x 4 =	69	4 x 1 =	94	4 x 3 =
20	1 x 4 =	45	6 x 4 =	70	10 x 4 =	95	10 x 4 =
21	2 x 4 =	46	4 x 10 =	71	4 x 4 =	96	4 x 5 =
22	4 x 9 =	47	8 x 4 =	72	6 x 4 =	97	8 x 4 =
23	3 x 4 =	48	4 x 5 =	73	4 x 2 =	98	4 x 0 =
24	4 x 7 =	49	3 x 4 =	74	7 x 4 =	99	2 x 4 =
25	4 x 4 =	50	1 x 4 =	75	1 x 4 =	100	4 x 6 =

Time? / Time? / Time? / Time?

Did you beat your score? / Which facts do you find the hardest? / Is this your best score? / Try to concentrate even more?

© **Topical Resources.** May be photocopied for classroom use only.

Exercise 8A	Exercise 8B	Exercise 8C	Exercise 8D
Name:	Name:	Name:	Name:
Date:	Date:	Date:	Date:

1 6 x 6 =	**26** 0 x 6 =	**51** 3 x 6 =	**76** 5 x 6 =
2 3 x 6 =	**27** 6 x 4 =	**52** 6 x 5 =	**77** 6 x 2 =
3 6 x 9 =	**28** 9 x 6 =	**53** 9 x 6 =	**78** 8 x 6 =
4 10 x 6 =	**29** 6 x 1 =	**54** 6 x 3 =	**79** 6 x 6 =
5 6 x 7 =	**30** 5 x 6 =	**55** 0 x 6 =	**80** 6 x 10 =
6 4 x 6 =	**31** 6 x 10 =	**56** 4 x 6 =	**81** 3 x 6 =
7 6 x 0 =	**32** 1 x 6 =	**57** 6 x 1 =	**82** 6 x 7 =
8 8 x 6 =	**33** 6 x 6 =	**58** 6 x 6 =	**83** 9 x 6 =
9 3 x 6 =	**34** 2 x 6 =	**59** 6 x 10 =	**84** 6 x 4 =
10 6 x 5 =	**35** 6 x 0 =	**60** 10 x 6 =	**85** 8 x 6 =
11 1 x 6 =	**36** 7 x 6 =	**61** 6 x 2 =	**86** 5 x 6 =
12 6 x 9 =	**37** 1 x 6 =	**62** 4 x 6 =	**87** 6 x 0 =
13 8 x 6 =	**38** 6 x 3 =	**63** 6 x 9 =	**88** 5 x 6 =
14 5 x 6 =	**39** 8 x 6 =	**64** 3 x 6 =	**89** 3 x 6 =
15 6 x 2 =	**40** 2 x 6 =	**65** 6 x 0 =	**90** 6 x 1 =
16 10 x 6 =	**41** 6 x 4 =	**66** 7 x 6 =	**91** 9 x 6 =
17 6 x 6 =	**42** 6 x 9 =	**67** 4 x 6 =	**92** 6 x 6 =
18 9 x 6 =	**43** 5 x 6 =	**68** 6 x 8 =	**93** 2 x 6 =
19 0 x 6 =	**44** 6 x 2 =	**69** 1 x 6 =	**94** 6 x 4 =
20 6 x 3 =	**45** 6 x 8 =	**70** 6 x 5 =	**95** 10 x 6 =
21 7 x 6 =	**46** 10 x 6 =	**71** 8 x 6 =	**96** 6 x 3 =
22 1 x 6 =	**47** 6 x 6 =	**72** 6 x 6 =	**97** 0 x 6 =
23 6 x 8 =	**48** 0 x 6 =	**73** 6 x 2 =	**98** 6 x 7 =
24 2 x 6 =	**49** 6 x 3 =	**74** 5 x 6 =	**99** 6 x 4 =
25 6 x 4 =	**50** 7 x 6 =	**75** 6 x 7 =	**100** 1 x 6 =

Exercise 8A	Exercise 8B	Exercise 8C	Exercise 8D
Time?	Time?	Time?	Time?
Is this your best score yet?	Did you beat your target?	Have you reached your target yet?	How do you think you are doing?

Exercise 9A	Exercise 9B	Exercise 9C	Exercise 9D
Name:	Name:	Name:	Name:
Date:	Date:	Date:	Date:
1. $7 \times 4 =$	26. $8 \times 7 =$	51. $7 \times 6 =$	76. $7 \times 0 =$
2. $10 \times 7 =$	27. $7 \times 0 =$	52. $8 \times 7 =$	77. $9 \times 7 =$
3. $7 \times 8 =$	28. $3 \times 7 =$	53. $7 \times 2 =$	78. $7 \times 1 =$
4. $1 \times 7 =$	29. $1 \times 7 =$	54. $7 \times 7 =$	79. $4 \times 7 =$
5. $7 \times 0 =$	30. $7 \times 9 =$	55. $3 \times 7 =$	80. $7 \times 10 =$
6. $5 \times 7 =$	31. $7 \times 1 =$	56. $7 \times 9 =$	81. $2 \times 7 =$
7. $9 \times 7 =$	32. $4 \times 7 =$	57. $8 \times 7 =$	82. $6 \times 7 =$
8. $7 \times 1 =$	33. $8 \times 7 =$	58. $7 \times 0 =$	83. $7 \times 3 =$
9. $4 \times 7 =$	34. $7 \times 2 =$	59. $7 \times 3 =$	84. $0 \times 7 =$
10. $6 \times 7 =$	35. $10 \times 7 =$	60. $1 \times 7 =$	85. $7 \times 0 =$
11. $7 \times 0 =$	36. $7 \times 9 =$	61. $7 \times 9 =$	86. $4 \times 7 =$
12. $2 \times 7 =$	37. $5 \times 7 =$	62. $7 \times 7 =$	87. $7 \times 6 =$
13. $7 \times 5 =$	38. $7 \times 3 =$	63. $4 \times 7 =$	88. $7 \times 7 =$
14. $10 \times 7 =$	39. $6 \times 7 =$	64. $7 \times 2 =$	89. $1 \times 7 =$
15. $7 \times 7 =$	40. $10 \times 7 =$	65. $10 \times 7 =$	90. $0 \times 7 =$
16. $7 \times 1 =$	41. $7 \times 0 =$	66. $7 \times 4 =$	91. $7 \times 5 =$
17. $6 \times 7 =$	42. $4 \times 7 =$	67. $7 \times 5 =$	92. $8 \times 7 =$
18. $3 \times 7 =$	43. $7 \times 6 =$	68. $3 \times 7 =$	93. $7 \times 2 =$
19. $7 \times 8 =$	44. $7 \times 1 =$	69. $7 \times 0 =$	94. $5 \times 7 =$
20. $2 \times 7 =$	45. $7 \times 5 =$	70. $10 \times 7 =$	95. $7 \times 10 =$
21. $7 \times 0 =$	46. $7 \times 7 =$	71. $7 \times 1 =$	96. $6 \times 7 =$
22. $9 \times 7 =$	47. $7 \times 0 =$	72. $6 \times 7 =$	97. $3 \times 7 =$
23. $7 \times 7 =$	48. $6 \times 7 =$	73. $7 \times 4 =$	98. $7 \times 7 =$
24. $4 \times 7 =$	49. $7 \times 2 =$	74. $1 \times 7 =$	99. $9 \times 7 =$
25. $7 \times 3 =$	50. $7 \times 7 =$	75. $5 \times 7 =$	100. $7 \times 8 =$
Time?	Time?	Time?	Time?

Try to be even quicker next time!

Can you try to be faster?

Did you do well?

What have you learnt today?

Exercise 10A	Exercise 10B	Exercise 10C	Exercise 10D
Name:	Name:	Name:	Name:
Date:	Date:	Date:	Date:

#	10A	#	10B	#	10C	#	10D
1	8 x 7 =	26	8 x 4 =	51	7 x 8 =	76	8 x 9 =
2	2 x 8 =	27	8 x 8 =	52	1 x 8 =	77	7 x 8 =
3	9 x 8 =	28	8 x 3 =	53	8 x 0 =	78	8 x 0 =
4	8 x 0 =	29	8 x 0 =	54	5 x 8 =	79	4 x 8 =
5	1 x 8 =	30	5 x 8 =	55	8 x 9 =	80	8 x 6 =
6	8 x 3 =	31	8 x 10 =	56	1 x 8 =	81	8 x 1 =
7	8 x 8 =	32	7 x 8 =	57	7 x 8 =	82	8 x 8 =
8	8 x 1 =	33	8 x 9 =	58	8 x 2 =	83	8 x 2 =
9	10 x 8 =	34	1 x 8 =	59	4 x 8 =	84	5 x 8 =
10	4 x 8 =	35	8 x 4 =	60	8 x 6 =	85	10 x 8 =
11	8 x 9 =	36	6 x 8 =	61	10 x 8 =	86	8 x 4 =
12	2 x 8 =	37	8 x 2 =	62	8 x 2 =	87	7 x 8 =
13	8 x 7 =	38	8 x 8 =	63	3 x 8 =	88	8 x 3 =
14	4 x 8 =	39	10 x 8 =	64	8 x 8 =	89	1 x 8 =
15	8 x 3 =	40	8 x 0 =	65	1 x 8 =	90	5 x 8 =
16	5 x 8 =	41	5 x 8 =	66	7 x 8 =	91	8 x 0 =
17	8 x 10 =	42	8 x 7 =	67	8 x 4 =	92	4 x 8 =
18	4 x 8 =	43	3 x 8 =	68	9 x 8 =	93	8 x 8 =
19	8 x 8 =	44	8 x 1 =	69	8 x 3 =	94	2 x 8 =
20	8 x 6 =	45	8 x 9 =	70	8 x 8 =	95	8 x 0 =
21	0 x 8 =	46	6 x 8 =	71	8 x 10 =	96	8 x 5 =
22	8 x 5 =	47	8 x 5 =	72	5 x 8 =	97	9 x 8 =
23	7 x 8 =	48	2 x 8 =	73	8 x 4 =	98	8 x 3 =
24	8 x 1 =	49	10 x 8 =	74	0 x 8 =	99	6 x 8 =
25	6 x 8 =	50	8 x 7 =	75	6 x 8 =	100	10 x 8 =

Time?	Time?	Time?	Time?
Did you use strategies?	Where can you improve?	Are you improving?	Did you do well?

Exercise 11A	Exercise 11B	Exercise 11C	Exercise 11D
Name:	Name:	Name:	Name:
Date:	Date:	Date:	Date:

1 1 x 10 =	**26** 10 x 7 =	**51** 9 x 10 =	**76** 9 x 2 =
2 9 x 10 =	**27** 4 x 10 =	**52** 2 x 8 =	**77** 0 x 10 =
3 10 x 0 =	**28** 10 x 9 =	**53** 10 x 7 =	**78** 2 x 8 =
4 4 x 2 =	**29** 10 x 6 =	**54** 6 x 2 =	**79** 10 x 10 =
5 2 x 10 =	**30** 3 x 10 =	**55** 10 x 10 =	**80** 10 x 2 =
6 2 x 7 =	**31** 10 x 4 =	**56** 5 x 10 =	**81** 7 x 10 =
7 10 x 3 =	**32** 9 x 2 =	**57** 2 x 4 =	**82** 2 x 8 =
8 7 x 10 =	**33** 8 x 2 =	**58** 10 x 8 =	**83** 7 x 2 =
9 9 x 2 =	**34** 10 x 7 =	**59** 10 x 2 =	**84** 10 x 1 =
10 10 x 7 =	**35** 4 x 10 =	**60** 1 x 10 =	**85** 2 x 6 =
11 2 x 8 =	**36** 2 x 6 =	**61** 2 x 3 =	**86** 5 x 10 =
12 4 x 10 =	**37** 8 x 10 =	**62** 3 x 10 =	**87** 10 x 9 =
13 10 x 8 =	**38** 10 x 9 =	**63** 9 x 2 =	**88** 1 x 2 =
14 4 x 2 =	**39** 4 x 10 =	**64** 10 x 6 =	**89** 2 x 10 =
15 10 x 10 =	**40** 10 x 2 =	**65** 2 x 2 =	**90** 2 x 4 =
16 2 x 3 =	**41** 7 x 10 =	**66** 8 x 2 =	**91** 10 x 6 =
17 10 x 5 =	**42** 10 x 9 =	**67** 0 x 10 =	**92** 8 x 2 =
18 6 x 2 =	**43** 10 x 10 =	**68** 2 x 7 =	**93** 2 x 10 =
19 8 x 10 =	**44** 6 x 10 =	**69** 10 x 4 =	**94** 2 x 2 =
20 2 x 2 =	**45** 8 x 2 =	**70** 1 x 2 =	**95** 10 x 3 =
21 10 x 4 =	**46** 10 x 10 =	**71** 1 x 10 =	**96** 7 x 10 =
22 7 x 10 =	**47** 2 x 7 =	**72** 10 x 8 =	**97** 5 x 2 =
23 9 x 10 =	**48** 10 x 1 =	**73** 2 x 4 =	**98** 8 x 10 =
24 1 x 2 =	**49** 4 x 2 =	**74** 7 x 2 =	**99** 2 x 3 =
25 10 x 6 =	**50** 10 x 0 =	**75** 2 x 10 =	**100** 10 x 4 =

Time?	Time?	Time?	Time?

How did you do?   Did you beat your best score?   Can you try to be faster?   Have you reached your target?

Exercise 12A	Exercise 12B	Exercise 12C	Exercise 12D
Name:	Name:	Name:	Name:
Date:	Date:	Date:	Date:

1 3 x 10 =	26 7 x 10 =	51 1 x 10 =	76 6 x 10 =
2 5 x 6 =	27 5 x 5 =	52 5 x 2 =	77 5 x 8 =
3 10 x 7 =	28 10 x 1 =	53 10 x 4 =	78 10 x 10 =
4 9 x 10 =	29 2 x 5 =	54 7 x 10 =	79 3 x 5 =
5 2 x 5 =	30 3 x 10 =	55 9 x 5 =	80 8 x 10 =
6 10 x 5 =	31 2 x 5 =	56 10 x 6 =	81 1 x 10 =
7 5 x 6 =	32 10 x 8 =	57 2 x 10 =	82 5 x 9 =
8 5 x 10 =	33 6 x 5 =	58 5 x 3 =	83 10 x 2 =
9 7 x 5 =	34 4 x 10 =	59 2 x 10 =	84 6 x 5 =
10 10 x 4 =	35 10 x 10 =	60 8 x 5 =	85 4 x 5 =
11 3 x 5 =	36 10 x 5 =	61 10 x 7 =	86 7 x 10 =
12 0 x 10 =	37 9 x 10 =	62 5 x 4 =	87 10 x 5 =
13 7 x 5 =	38 5 x 0 =	63 5 x 10 =	88 10 x 3 =
14 6 x 10 =	39 7 x 5 =	64 7 x 5 =	89 5 x 5 =
15 5 x 9 =	40 0 x 10 =	65 10 x 1 =	90 9 x 10 =
16 10 x 8 =	41 5 x 1 =	66 10 x 8 =	91 1 x 5 =
17 10 x 1 =	42 10 x 5 =	67 5 x 6 =	92 10 x 8 =
18 4 x 5 =	43 8 x 5 =	68 5 x 5 =	93 5 x 6 =
19 5 x 10 =	44 10 x 10 =	69 6 x 10 =	94 10 x 10 =
20 5 x 8 =	45 5 x 7 =	70 9 x 5 =	95 7 x 5 =
21 10 x 10 =	46 10 x 1 =	71 10 x 9 =	96 10 x 4 =
22 5 x 5 =	47 4 x 5 =	72 5 x 6 =	97 5 x 2 =
23 6 x 10 =	48 6 x 10 =	73 3 x 10 =	98 5 x 10 =
24 5 x 1 =	49 5 x 9 =	74 7 x 5 =	99 7 x 5 =
25 10 x 5 =	50 10 x 5 =	75 10 x 10 =	100 9 x 10 =

Time?	Time?	Time?	Time?

How do you think you are doing? How did you do? Is this your best score? Which facts do you find the easiest?

Exercise 13A	Exercise 13B	Exercise 13C	Exercise 13D
Name:	Name:	Name:	Name:
Date:	Date:	Date:	Date:

#	A	#	B	#	C	#	D
1	1 x 2 =	26	5 x 2 =	51	4 x 2 =	76	4 x 2 =
2	5 x 7 =	27	4 x 5 =	52	5 x 9 =	77	8 x 5 =
3	2 x 4 =	28	9 x 2 =	53	2 x 8 =	78	2 x 9 =
4	6 x 2 =	29	5 x 7 =	54	1 x 2 =	79	5 x 7 =
5	2 x 5 =	30	6 x 2 =	55	10 x 5 =	80	5 x 2 =
6	5 x 8 =	31	3 x 5 =	56	2 x 0 =	81	10 x 2 =
7	7 x 2 =	32	2 x 0 =	57	5 x 4 =	82	9 x 5 =
8	3 x 5 =	33	5 x 8 =	58	5 x 2 =	83	2 x 6 =
9	2 x 0 =	34	10 x 2 =	59	7 x 5 =	84	8 x 5 =
10	5 x 9 =	35	4 x 5 =	60	2 x 1 =	85	0 x 2 =
11	8 x 2 =	36	1 x 2 =	61	5 x 6 =	86	5 x 4 =
12	4 x 5 =	37	5 x 7 =	62	9 x 2 =	87	2 x 4 =
13	2 x 8 =	38	7 x 2 =	63	8 x 5 =	88	10 x 5 =
14	5 x 10 =	39	2 x 2 =	64	6 x 2 =	89	7 x 2 =
15	2 x 2 =	40	0 x 5 =	65	4 x 5 =	90	5 x 5 =
16	0 x 5 =	41	5 x 5 =	66	2 x 2 =	91	1 x 2 =
17	5 x 2 =	42	7 x 2 =	67	2 x 10 =	92	9 x 5 =
18	5 x 5 =	43	5 x 1 =	68	5 x 5 =	93	0 x 5 =
19	2 x 9 =	44	2 x 3 =	69	5 x 9 =	94	5 x 2 =
20	6 x 5 =	45	6 x 5 =	70	0 x 2 =	95	5 x 6 =
21	10 x 2 =	46	8 x 2 =	71	6 x 5 =	96	2 x 2 =
22	5 x 1 =	47	5 x 7 =	72	2 x 3 =	97	1 x 5 =
23	3 x 2 =	48	2 x 4 =	73	5 x 10 =	98	8 x 2 =
24	5 x 5 =	49	2 x 5 =	74	7 x 2 =	99	5 x 7 =
25	2 x 10 =	50	8 x 2 =	75	8 x 5 =	100	3 x 2 =

Time?	Time?	Time?	Time?
Did you do well?	What have you learnt today?	Have you reached your target?	What is your time?

Exercise 14A	Exercise 14B	Exercise 14C	Exercise 14D
Name:	Name:	Name:	Name:
Date:	Date:	Date:	Date:

1 4 x 4 =	**26** 0 x 0 =	**51** 7 x 7 =	**76** 3 x 3 =
2 5 x 9 =	**27** 8 x 8 =	**52** 4 x 9 =	**77** 0 x 0 =
3 9 x 7 =	**28** 9 x 4 =	**53** 6 x 6 =	**78** 9 x 4 =
4 3 x 3 =	**29** 6 x 6 =	**54** 1 x 1 =	**79** 6 x 6 =
5 7 x 7 =	**30** 9 x 9 =	**55** 9 x 7 =	**80** 3 x 9 =
6 6 x 9 =	**31** 1 x 1 =	**56** 8 x 8 =	**81** 1 x 1 =
7 8 x 8 =	**32** 9 x 5 =	**57** 3 x 9 =	**82** 9 x 7 =
8 9 x 0 =	**33** 10 x 10 =	**58** 1 x 1 =	**83** 2 x 2 =
9 6 x 6 =	**34** 10 x 9 =	**59** 10 x 10 =	**84** 5 x 9 =
10 9 x 10 =	**35** 5 x 5 =	**60** 9 x 2 =	**85** 7 x 7 =
11 7 x 9 =	**36** 9 x 4 =	**61** 3 x 3 =	**86** 9 x 3 =
12 1 x 1 =	**37** 7 x 7 =	**62** 7 x 7 =	**87** 5 x 5 =
13 9 x 1 =	**38** 2 x 2 =	**63** 8 x 9 =	**88** 6 x 9 =
14 10 x 10 =	**39** 6 x 9 =	**64** 4 x 4 =	**89** 10 x 10 =
15 9 x 9 =	**40** 6 x 6 =	**65** 9 x 1 =	**90** 9 x 8 =
16 5 x 5 =	**41** 9 x 3 =	**66** 0 x 0 =	**91** 1 x 1 =
17 7 x 7 =	**42** 1 x 1 =	**67** 9 x 9 =	**92** 6 x 6 =
18 9 x 2 =	**43** 0 x 0 =	**68** 6 x 6 =	**93** 7 x 9 =
19 2 x 2 =	**44** 7 x 9 =	**69** 9 x 3 =	**94** 8 x 8 =
20 3 x 9 =	**45** 4 x 4 =	**70** 2 x 2 =	**95** 9 x 9 =
21 6 x 6 =	**46** 9 x 2 =	**71** 10 x 9 =	**96** 3 x 3 =
22 9 x 8 =	**47** 3 x 3 =	**72** 7 x 7 =	**97** 7 x 7 =
23 1 x 1 =	**48** 7 x 7 =	**73** 0 x 9 =	**98** 9 x 10 =
24 4 x 9 =	**49** 8 x 9 =	**74** 9 x 9 =	**99** 4 x 4 =
25 0 x 0 =	**50** 5 x 5 =	**75** 10 x 10 =	**100** 8 x 9 =

Time?	Time?	Time?	Time?

Try to be even quicker next time?

How are you doing?

Try to be faster?

Did you beat your target?

Exercise 15A	Exercise 15B	Exercise 15C	Exercise 15D
Name:	Name:	Name:	Name:
Date:	Date:	Date:	Date:

Exercise 15A	Exercise 15B	Exercise 15C	Exercise 15D
1 3 x 4 =	**26** 0 x 3 =	**51** 7 x 3 =	**76** 8 x 3 =
2 4 x 4 =	**27** 3 x 5 =	**52** 1 x 4 =	**77** 4 x 4 =
3 8 x 3 =	**28** 6 x 4 =	**53** 3 x 9 =	**78** 3 x 10 =
4 9 x 4 =	**29** 1 x 3 =	**54** 7 x 4 =	**79** 8 x 4 =
5 1 x 3 =	**30** 9 x 4 =	**55** 5 x 3 =	**80** 0 x 3 =
6 5 x 3 =	**31** 3 x 6 =	**56** 2 x 3 =	**81** 5 x 3 =
7 3 x 0 =	**32** 9 x 3 =	**57** 4 x 2 =	**82** 4 x 9 =
8 5 x 4 =	**33** 7 x 4 =	**58** 3 x 6 =	**83** 3 x 3 =
9 2 x 3 =	**34** 7 x 3 =	**59** 8 x 4 =	**84** 6 x 4 =
10 3 x 9 =	**35** 4 x 0 =	**60** 10 x 3 =	**85** 0 x 3 =
11 1 x 3 =	**36** 3 x 2 =	**61** 4 x 3 =	**86** 4 x 10 =
12 0 x 4 =	**37** 5 x 4 =	**62** 3 x 0 =	**87** 3 x 6 =
13 6 x 3 =	**38** 8 x 3 =	**63** 7 x 3 =	**88** 1 x 3 =
14 4 x 8 =	**39** 4 x 1 =	**64** 4 x 4 =	**89** 5 x 4 =
15 3 x 0 =	**40** 3 x 10 =	**65** 3 x 0 =	**90** 3 x 1 =
16 1 x 4 =	**41** 8 x 4 =	**66** 4 x 9 =	**91** 7 x 3 =
17 3 x 3 =	**42** 1 x 3 =	**67** 1 x 3 =	**92** 0 x 4 =
18 4 x 6 =	**43** 10 x 4 =	**68** 5 x 4 =	**93** 3 x 2 =
19 2 x 3 =	**44** 3 x 3 =	**69** 3 x 8 =	**94** 2 x 3 =
20 2 x 4 =	**45** 2 x 4 =	**70** 4 x 10 =	**95** 4 x 4 =
21 3 x 10 =	**46** 3 x 0 =	**71** 1 x 3 =	**96** 3 x 8 =
22 4 x 7 =	**47** 4 x 3 =	**72** 6 x 4 =	**97** 4 x 1 =
23 3 x 3 =	**48** 6 x 3 =	**73** 3 x 2 =	**98** 3 x 3 =
24 3 x 4 =	**49** 4 x 4 =	**74** 4 x 0 =	**99** 4 x 7 =
25 3 x 7 =	**50** 4 x 3 =	**75** 3 x 3 =	**100** 9 x 3 =

Time?	Time?	Time?	Time?

Do you think you are improving?

Are the facts at your fingertips?

Try to really focus!

Try to be faster?

Exercise 16A	Exercise 16B	Exercise 16C	Exercise 16D
Name:	Name:	Name:	Name:
Date:	Date:	Date:	Date:

#	16A	#	16B	#	16C	#	16D
1	6 x 3 =	26	6 x 0 =	51	5 x 6 =	76	5 x 6 =
2	4 x 7 =	27	7 x 3 =	52	7 x 8 =	77	7 x 4 =
3	10 x 6 =	28	6 x 6 =	53	6 x 9 =	78	6 x 6 =
4	7 x 5 =	29	7 x 7 =	54	3 x 7 =	79	10 x 7 =
5	6 x 1 =	30	6 x 10 =	55	7 x 6 =	80	0 x 6 =
6	4 x 6 =	31	4 x 7 =	56	9 x 7 =	81	5 x 7 =
7	6 x 7 =	32	1 x 6 =	57	6 x 0 =	82	6 x 7 =
8	6 x 0 =	33	7 x 8 =	58	6 x 6 =	83	7 x 4 =
9	7 x 2 =	34	6 x 7 =	59	10 x 7 =	84	1 x 6 =
10	5 x 6 =	35	7 x 5 =	60	6 x 10 =	85	6 x 7 =
11	1 x 7 =	36	2 x 6 =	61	4 x 7 =	86	6 x 8 =
12	6 x 0 =	37	7 x 0 =	62	1 x 6 =	87	7 x 0 =
13	7 x 8 =	38	6 x 8 =	63	6 x 7 =	88	2 x 6 =
14	1 x 6 =	39	3 x 6 =	64	7 x 0 =	89	7 x 7 =
15	2 x 7 =	40	7 x 9 =	65	4 x 6 =	90	6 x 9 =
16	6 x 6 =	41	6 x 0 =	66	5 x 7 =	91	7 x 1 =
17	7 x 7 =	42	1 x 7 =	67	6 x 2 =	92	3 x 6 =
18	7 x 6 =	43	4 x 6 =	68	7 x 1 =	93	8 x 7 =
19	6 x 10 =	44	7 x 10 =	69	8 x 6 =	94	6 x 10 =
20	8 x 6 =	45	6 x 1 =	70	6 x 5 =	95	0 x 6 =
21	3 x 7 =	46	4 x 7 =	71	2 x 7 =	96	7 x 2 =
22	2 x 6 =	47	7 x 2 =	72	3 x 6 =	97	6 x 4 =
23	7 x 3 =	48	5 x 6 =	73	7 x 6 =	98	9 x 7 =
24	9 x 6 =	49	6 x 7 =	74	6 x 4 =	99	1 x 6 =
25	4 x 7 =	50	6 x 9 =	75	7 x 7 =	100	7 x 3 =

Time?	Time?	Time?	Time?
What is your time?	How did you do?	Is this your fastest time?	Did you reach your target?

Exercise 17A	Exercise 17B	Exercise 17C	Exercise 17D
Name:	Name:	Name:	Name:
Date:	Date:	Date:	Date:

1 4 x 7 =	**26** 7 x 4 =	**51** 2 x 7 =	**76** 5 x 7 =
2 8 x 5 =	**27** 3 x 8 =	**52** 8 x 5 =	**77** 8 x 8 =
3 7 x 8 =	**28** 9 x 7 =	**53** 8 x 10 =	**78** 7 x 9 =
4 6 x 8 =	**29** 8 x 7 =	**54** 7 x 8 =	**79** 8 x 3 =
5 4 x 7 =	**30** 7 x 5 =	**55** 6 x 8 =	**80** 0 x 7 =
6 0 x 7 =	**31** 4 x 8 =	**56** 8 x 4 =	**81** 4 x 7 =
7 8 x 6 =	**32** 1 x 7 =	**57** 3 x 7 =	**82** 9 x 8 =
8 7 x 5 =	**33** 8 x 8 =	**58** 7 x 9 =	**83** 8 x 10 =
9 7 x 8 =	**34** 5 x 8 =	**59** 0 x 8 =	**84** 7 x 1 =
10 8 x 1 =	**35** 0 x 7 =	**60** 4 x 7 =	**85** 4 x 8 =
11 1 x 7 =	**36** 5 x 8 =	**61** 8 x 7 =	**86** 6 x 7 =
12 7 x 8 =	**37** 6 x 7 =	**62** 7 x 10 =	**87** 8 x 0 =
13 7 x 9 =	**38** 7 x 10 =	**63** 1 x 8 =	**88** 7 x 10 =
14 8 x 2 =	**39** 8 x 0 =	**64** 4 x 7 =	**89** 8 x 5 =
15 8 x 8 =	**40** 1 x 7 =	**65** 8 x 8 =	**90** 2 x 7 =
16 2 x 7 =	**41** 9 x 8 =	**66** 7 x 0 =	**91** 1 x 8 =
17 8 x 8 =	**42** 7 x 7 =	**67** 2 x 8 =	**92** 7 x 7 =
18 7 x 6 =	**43** 0 x 7 =	**68** 5 x 7 =	**93** 4 x 8 =
19 8 x 3 =	**44** 6 x 8 =	**69** 8 x 9 =	**94** 3 x 7 =
20 10 x 7 =	**45** 7 x 2 =	**70** 8 x 7 =	**95** 8 x 6 =
21 9 x 8 =	**46** 8 x 1 =	**71** 3 x 8 =	**96** 7 x 0 =
22 3 x 7 =	**47** 8 x 7 =	**72** 6 x 7 =	**97** 7 x 8 =
23 8 x 4 =	**48** 10 x 8 =	**73** 7 x 1 =	**98** 8 x 7 =
24 7 x 7 =	**49** 7 x 3 =	**74** 4 x 8 =	**99** 8 x 2 =
25 10 x 8 =	**50** 8 x 2 =	**75** 7 x 7 =	**100** 7 x 4 =

Time?	Time?	Time?	Time?
Which facts did you find the hardest?	Did you beat your target?	Can you try to be faster?	Where do you need to improve?

Exercise 18A	Exercise 18B	Exercise 18C	Exercise 18D
Name:	Name:	Name:	Name:
Date:	Date:	Date:	Date:

1. 1 x 2 =	26. 0 x 1 =	51. 1 x 6 =	76. 7 x 1 =
2. 10 x 1 =	27. 1 x 4 =	52. 5 x 0 =	77. 0 x 9 =
3. 3 x 0 =	28. 9 x 1 =	53. 1 x 10 =	78. 6 x 1 =
4. 1 x 7 =	29. 0 x 3 =	54. 1 x 9 =	79. 0 x 8 =
5. 4 x 0 =	30. 10 x 1 =	55. 7 x 0 =	80. 0 x 3 =
6. 1 x 1 =	31. 1 x 2 =	56. 1 x 8 =	81. 8 x 1 =
7. 3 x 1 =	32. 4 x 0 =	57. 1 x 4 =	82. 0 x 7 =
8. 0 x 7 =	33. 1 x 5 =	58. 6 x 0 =	83. 0 x 4 =
9. 0 x 9 =	34. 8 x 0 =	59. 7 x 1 =	84. 9 x 1 =
10. 10 x 1 =	35. 3 x 0 =	60. 0 x 10 =	85. 2 x 1 =
11. 0 x 6 =	36. 1 x 5 =	61. 1 x 8 =	86. 1 x 6 =
12. 5 x 1 =	37. 9 x 1 =	62. 7 x 0 =	87. 8 x 0 =
13. 1 x 8 =	38. 0 x 2 =	63. 1 x 5 =	88. 1 x 10 =
14. 10 x 0 =	39. 7 x 0 =	64. 1 x 4 =	89. 3 x 0 =
15. 7 x 1 =	40. 1 x 2 =	65. 1 x 0 =	90. 1 x 9 =
16. 0 x 1 =	41. 1 x 8 =	66. 1 x 7 =	91. 7 x 0 =
17. 7 x 0 =	42. 4 x 0 =	67. 3 x 1 =	92. 1 x 9 =
18. 1 x 3 =	43. 1 x 2 =	68. 0 x 8 =	93. 1 x 3 =
19. 6 x 0 =	44. 9 x 0 =	69. 4 x 1 =	94. 10 x 0 =
20. 1 x 6 =	45. 3 x 0 =	70. 6 x 1 =	95. 1 x 0 =
21. 4 x 1 =	46. 1 x 5 =	71. 0 x 2 =	96. 1 x 3 =
22. 0 x 6 =	47. 10 x 1 =	72. 6 x 0 =	97. 7 x 1 =
23. 0 x 5 =	48. 0 x 4 =	73. 1 x 10 =	98. 0 x 1 =
24. 4 x 1 =	49. 5 x 1 =	74. 2 x 1 =	99. 4 x 0 =
25. 6 x 1 =	50. 0 x 1 =	75. 0 x 3 =	100. 1 x 2 =

Time?	Time?	Time?	Time?
Is this your best score?	Have you reached your target?	Did you do well?	Do you think you are improving?

Exercise 19A	Exercise 19B	Exercise 19C	Exercise 19D
Name:	Name:	Name:	Name:
Date:	Date:	Date:	Date:

1 7 x 1 =	**26** 10 x 10 =	**51** 10 x 7 =	**76** 0 x 7 =
2 8 x 0 =	**27** 1 x 9 =	**52** 0 x 9 =	**77** 0 x 8 =
3 1 x 10 =	**28** 4 x 1 =	**53** 10 x 1 =	**78** 10 x 6 =
4 1 x 6 =	**29** 10 x 8 =	**54** 6 x 10 =	**79** 6 x 1 =
5 7 x 1 =	**30** 6 x 1 =	**55** 0 x 2 =	**80** 4 x 10 =
6 10 x 9 =	**31** 3 x 10 =	**56** 1 x 1 =	**81** 1 x 9 =
7 0 x 3 =	**32** 0 x 7 =	**57** 10 x 5 =	**82** 5 x 0 =
8 1 x 10 =	**33** 10 x 1 =	**58** 4 x 1 =	**83** 10 x 5 =
9 5 x 0 =	**34** 6 x 1 =	**59** 0 x 4 =	**84** 0 x 10 =
10 1 x 5 =	**35** 2 x 1 =	**60** 4 x 10 =	**85** 10 x 10 =
11 2 x 10 =	**36** 5 x 10 =	**61** 3 x 1 =	**86** 8 x 1 =
12 10 x 1 =	**37** 1 x 4 =	**62** 6 x 1 =	**87** 1 x 9 =
13 0 x 9 =	**38** 6 x 0 =	**63** 10 x 3 =	**88** 10 x 9 =
14 10 x 4 =	**39** 10 x 3 =	**64** 0 x 8 =	**89** 1 x 0 =
15 3 x 1 =	**40** 1 x 5 =	**65** 0 x 4 =	**90** 8 x 10 =
16 0 x 7 =	**41** 8 x 0 =	**66** 2 x 10 =	**91** 0 x 10 =
17 6 x 10 =	**42** 9 x 10 =	**67** 7 x 1 =	**92** 10 x 10 =
18 10 x 1 =	**43** 0 x 8 =	**68** 10 x 9 =	**93** 2 x 1 =
19 10 x 3 =	**44** 6 x 0 =	**69** 3 x 1 =	**94** 7 x 1 =
20 0 x 4 =	**45** 10 x 8 =	**70** 5 x 10 =	**95** 1 x 10 =
21 5 x 1 =	**46** 1 x 4 =	**71** 0 x 4 =	**96** 4 x 1 =
22 7 x 10 =	**47** 5 x 1 =	**72** 10 x 2 =	**97** 0 x 6 =
23 0 x 1 =	**48** 0 x 9 =	**73** 5 x 0 =	**98** 10 x 1 =
24 10 x 1 =	**49** 10 x 7 =	**74** 1 x 8 =	**99** 2 x 1 =
25 2 x 1 =	**50** 3 x 1 =	**75** 7 x 10 =	**100** 0 x 3 =

Time?	Time?	Time?	Time?
Try to concentrate even more!	How do you think you are doing?	What have you learnt today?	How could you recall these facts even quicker?

Exercise 20A	Exercise 20B	Exercise 20C	Exercise 20D
Name:	Name:	Name:	Name:
Date:	Date:	Date:	Date:

#		#		#		#	
1	$10 \times 3 =$	26	$0 \times 4 =$	51	$2 \times 9 =$	76	$7 \times 2 =$
2	$1 \times 5 =$	27	$2 \times 1 =$	52	$10 \times 1 =$	77	$10 \times 6 =$
3	$8 \times 0 =$	28	$10 \times 1 =$	53	$6 \times 0 =$	78	$1 \times 8 =$
4	$9 \times 10 =$	29	$2 \times 7 =$	54	$2 \times 10 =$	79	$2 \times 2 =$
5	$4 \times 2 =$	30	$0 \times 6 =$	55	$4 \times 2 =$	80	$4 \times 10 =$
6	$0 \times 7 =$	31	$1 \times 4 =$	56	$0 \times 8 =$	81	$1 \times 9 =$
7	$10 \times 8 =$	32	$7 \times 10 =$	57	$6 \times 0 =$	82	$5 \times 0 =$
8	$1 \times 4 =$	33	$2 \times 2 =$	58	$2 \times 3 =$	83	$8 \times 2 =$
9	$2 \times 7 =$	34	$0 \times 3 =$	59	$10 \times 8 =$	84	$10 \times 5 =$
10	$5 \times 1 =$	35	$8 \times 10 =$	60	$1 \times 4 =$	85	$10 \times 10 =$
11	$0 \times 9 =$	36	$6 \times 1 =$	61	$6 \times 2 =$	86	$2 \times 3 =$
12	$5 \times 2 =$	37	$2 \times 6 =$	62	$5 \times 1 =$	87	$1 \times 9 =$
13	$10 \times 7 =$	38	$0 \times 3 =$	63	$0 \times 9 =$	88	$9 \times 2 =$
14	$4 \times 10 =$	39	$10 \times 4 =$	64	$4 \times 10 =$	89	$8 \times 10 =$
15	$3 \times 1 =$	40	$1 \times 6 =$	65	$2 \times 7 =$	90	$0 \times 10 =$
16	$2 \times 8 =$	41	$4 \times 2 =$	66	$10 \times 7 =$	91	$2 \times 1 =$
17	$1 \times 6 =$	42	$4 \times 10 =$	67	$1 \times 1 =$	92	$2 \times 5 =$
18	$0 \times 6 =$	43	$0 \times 2 =$	68	$9 \times 2 =$	93	$7 \times 1 =$
19	$3 \times 2 =$	44	$2 \times 8 =$	69	$0 \times 4 =$	94	$0 \times 6 =$
20	$10 \times 9 =$	45	$1 \times 1 =$	70	$4 \times 10 =$	95	$4 \times 10 =$
21	$0 \times 4 =$	46	$10 \times 5 =$	71	$2 \times 8 =$	96	$4 \times 2 =$
22	$2 \times 9 =$	47	$9 \times 2 =$	72	$3 \times 1 =$	97	$3 \times 1 =$
23	$5 \times 1 =$	48	$3 \times 1 =$	73	$1 \times 4 =$	98	$0 \times 7 =$
24	$7 \times 10 =$	49	$10 \times 7 =$	74	$10 \times 6 =$	99	$2 \times 10 =$
25	$6 \times 2 =$	50	$6 \times 1 =$	75	$5 \times 2 =$	100	$2 \times 6 =$

Time?	Time?	Time?	Time?
Are the facts at your fingertips?	Try to really focus!	Which facts do you find the easiest?	Did you do well?

Exercise 21A	Exercise 21B	Exercise 21C	Exercise 21D
Name:	Name:	Name:	Name:
Date:	Date:	Date:	Date:

1 9 x 5 =	**26** 8 x 2 =	**51** 7 x 10 =	**76** 3 x 1 =
2 2 x 6 =	**27** 5 x 0 =	**52** 2 x 6 =	**77** 6 x 5 =
3 2 x 10 =	**28** 5 x 6 =	**53** 4 x 10 =	**78** 2 x 9 =
4 5 x 5 =	**29** 1 x 9 =	**54** 5 x 3 =	**79** 10 x 5 =
5 0 x 7 =	**30** 4 x 10 =	**55** 0 x 9 =	**80** 1 x 1 =
6 3 x 1 =	**31** 2 x 2 =	**56** 1 x 5 =	**81** 2 x 8 =
7 5 x 5 =	**32** 7 x 5 =	**57** 6 x 2 =	**82** 5 x 7 =
8 4 x 2 =	**33** 1 x 8 =	**58** 4 x 5 =	**83** 0 x 2 =
9 3 x 10 =	**34** 10 x 6 =	**59** 1 x 4 =	**84** 4 x 10 =
10 6 x 5 =	**35** 7 x 2 =	**60** 10 x 8 =	**85** 4 x 2 =
11 0 x 6 =	**36** 5 x 3 =	**61** 2 x 3 =	**86** 3 x 5 =
12 1 x 7 =	**37** 5 x 2 =	**62** 5 x 8 =	**87** 1 x 6 =
13 2 x 5 =	**38** 10 x 6 =	**63** 6 x 0 =	**88** 10 x 4 =
14 5 x 3 =	**39** 1 x 4 =	**64** 0 x 8 =	**89** 0 x 3 =
15 2 x 1 =	**40** 8 x 5 =	**65** 4 x 2 =	**90** 5 x 8 =
16 0 x 10 =	**41** 3 x 1 =	**66** 5 x 5 =	**91** 2 x 6 =
17 7 x 5 =	**42** 2 x 8 =	**67** 2 x 10 =	**92** 1 x 6 =
18 8 x 10 =	**43** 4 x 10 =	**68** 6 x 0 =	**93** 4 x 5 =
19 9 x 2 =	**44** 5 x 4 =	**69** 10 x 1 =	**94** 8 x 10 =
20 1 x 8 =	**45** 0 x 4 =	**70** 5 x 6 =	**95** 9 x 5 =
21 5 x 4 =	**46** 2 x 9 =	**71** 2 x 9 =	**96** 0 x 3 =
22 2 x 3 =	**47** 1 x 1 =	**72** 9 x 5 =	**97** 5 x 5 =
23 10 x 10 =	**48** 5 x 5 =	**73** 6 x 1 =	**98** 2 x 2 =
24 10 x 5 =	**49** 10 x 7 =	**74** 10 x 7 =	**99** 7 x 10 =
25 8 x 5 =	**50** 9 x 5 =	**75** 7 x 5 =	**100** 1 x 4 =

Time?	Time?	Time?	Time?
Did you beat you score?	Which facts do you find the hardest?	Is this your best score?	Try to concentrate even more?

Exercise 22A	Exercise 22B	Exercise 22C	Exercise 22D
Name:	Name:	Name:	Name:
Date:	Date:	Date:	Date:
1 $3 \times 3 =$	26 $9 \times 9 =$	51 $1 \times 1 =$	76 $8 \times 8 =$
2 $7 \times 5 =$	27 $10 \times 8 =$	52 $5 \times 4 =$	77 $1 \times 9 =$
3 $10 \times 7 =$	28 $1 \times 4 =$	53 $5 \times 5 =$	78 $5 \times 6 =$
4 $7 \times 7 =$	29 $3 \times 3 =$	54 $4 \times 10 =$	79 $3 \times 3 =$
5 $1 \times 6 =$	30 $4 \times 5 =$	55 $2 \times 8 =$	80 $5 \times 0 =$
6 $2 \times 2 =$	31 $6 \times 2 =$	56 $3 \times 1 =$	81 $8 \times 2 =$
7 $9 \times 5 =$	32 $7 \times 7 =$	57 $6 \times 6 =$	82 $9 \times 9 =$
8 $4 \times 4 =$	33 $1 \times 5 =$	58 $8 \times 5 =$	83 $8 \times 5 =$
9 $2 \times 9 =$	34 $4 \times 4 =$	59 $1 \times 4 =$	84 $10 \times 5 =$
10 $1 \times 1 =$	35 $0 \times 9 =$	60 $7 \times 7 =$	85 $1 \times 1 =$
11 $5 \times 6 =$	36 $5 \times 3 =$	61 $10 \times 6 =$	86 $2 \times 3 =$
12 $6 \times 6 =$	37 $2 \times 2 =$	62 $5 \times 2 =$	87 $5 \times 4 =$
13 $10 \times 1 =$	38 $4 \times 10 =$	63 $2 \times 2 =$	88 $4 \times 4 =$
14 $6 \times 0 =$	39 $2 \times 6 =$	64 $3 \times 5 =$	89 $1 \times 8 =$
15 $5 \times 5 =$	40 $1 \times 1 =$	65 $7 \times 2 =$	90 $10 \times 10 =$
16 $2 \times 10 =$	41 $8 \times 8 =$	66 $8 \times 8 =$	91 $9 \times 2 =$
17 $5 \times 5 =$	42 $7 \times 10 =$	67 $10 \times 6 =$	92 $5 \times 5 =$
18 $10 \times 10 =$	43 $6 \times 6 =$	68 $1 \times 8 =$	93 $8 \times 10 =$
19 $4 \times 2 =$	44 $9 \times 5 =$	69 $9 \times 9 =$	94 $7 \times 5 =$
20 $0 \times 8 =$	45 $10 \times 7 =$	70 $7 \times 5 =$	95 $2 \times 2 =$
21 $9 \times 9 =$	46 $5 \times 5 =$	71 $2 \times 2 =$	96 $0 \times 10 =$
22 $6 \times 1 =$	47 $1 \times 7 =$	72 $3 \times 3 =$	97 $6 \times 6 =$
23 $5 \times 8 =$	48 $2 \times 9 =$	73 $10 \times 10 =$	98 $2 \times 1 =$
24 $2 \times 3 =$	49 $10 \times 10 =$	74 $4 \times 10 =$	99 $5 \times 3 =$
25 $8 \times 8 =$	50 $0 \times 4 =$	75 $4 \times 4 =$	100 $7 \times 7 =$
Time?	Time?	Time?	Time?
Is this your best score yet?	Did you beat your target?	Have you reached your target yet?	How do you think you are doing?

Exercise 23A	Exercise 23B	Exercise 23C	Exercise 23D
Name:	Name:	Name:	Name:
Date:	Date:	Date:	Date:

	Exercise 23A		Exercise 23B		Exercise 23C		Exercise 23D
1	8 x 9 =	26	7 x 9 =	51	4 x 9 =	76	8 x 5 =
2	10 x 6 =	27	8 x 8 =	52	7 x 7 =	77	6 x 9 =
3	7 x 7 =	28	1 x 1 =	53	0 x 10 =	78	1 x 4 =
4	3 x 9 =	29	2 x 6 =	54	2 x 2 =	79	7 x 7 =
5	1 x 4 =	30	4 x 10 =	55	7 x 5 =	80	10 x 6 =
6	8 x 5 =	31	2 x 2 =	56	8 x 9 =	81	5 x 2 =
7	6 x 6 =	32	3 x 9 =	57	8 x 10 =	82	2 x 2 =
8	3 x 1 =	33	5 x 5 =	58	5 x 5 =	83	4 x 9 =
9	2 x 8 =	34	0 x 9 =	59	9 x 2 =	84	3 x 5 =
10	4 x 10 =	35	3 x 5 =	60	10 x 10 =	85	7 x 2 =
11	4 x 9 =	36	4 x 4 =	61	3 x 9 =	86	8 x 8 =
12	5 x 5 =	37	1 x 5 =	62	1 x 8 =	87	10 x 6 =
13	5 x 4 =	38	7 x 7 =	63	4 x 4 =	88	3 x 9 =
14	1 x 1 =	39	6 x 2 =	64	5 x 4 =	89	1 x 8 =
15	0 x 4 =	40	6 x 9 =	65	2 x 3 =	90	9 x 9 =
16	10 x 10 =	41	4 x 5 =	66	6 x 9 =	91	7 x 5 =
17	2 x 9 =	42	3 x 3 =	67	1 x 1 =	92	2 x 2 =
18	1 x 7 =	43	1 x 4 =	68	10 x 5 =	93	7 x 9 =
19	6 x 9 =	44	10 x 8 =	69	8 x 5 =	94	3 x 3 =
20	5 x 5 =	45	8 x 9 =	70	9 x 9 =	95	10 x 10 =
21	10 x 7 =	46	9 x 9 =	71	7 x 9 =	96	4 x 10 =
22	9 x 5 =	47	5 x 3 =	72	8 x 2 =	97	5 x 4 =
23	6 x 6 =	48	2 x 1 =	73	5 x 0 =	98	8 x 9 =
24	7 x 10 =	49	6 x 6 =	74	3 x 3 =	99	4 x 4 =
25	7 x 9 =	50	4 x 9 =	75	5 x 6 =	100	2 x 8 =

Time?	Time?	Time?	Time?

Try to be even quicker next time!

Can you try to be faster?

Did you do well?

What have you learnt today?

Exercise 24A	Exercise 24B	Exercise 24C	Exercise 24D
Name:	Name:	Name:	Name:
Date:	Date:	Date:	Date:

1. $3 \times 9 =$	26. $3 \times 5 =$	51. $4 \times 5 =$	76. $5 \times 5 =$
2. $7 \times 7 =$	27. $3 \times 9 =$	52. $3 \times 4 =$	77. $3 \times 5 =$
3. $1 \times 4 =$	28. $10 \times 10 =$	53. $6 \times 9 =$	78. $8 \times 9 =$
4. $6 \times 9 =$	29. $9 \times 2 =$	54. $6 \times 2 =$	79. $10 \times 6 =$
5. $3 \times 5 =$	30. $3 \times 6 =$	55. $7 \times 7 =$	80. $3 \times 7 =$
6. $8 \times 5 =$	31. $5 \times 5 =$	56. $2 \times 5 =$	81. $7 \times 7 =$
7. $5 \times 6 =$	32. $8 \times 10 =$	57. $1 \times 5 =$	82. $3 \times 9 =$
8. $3 \times 3 =$	33. $3 \times 3 =$	58. $4 \times 4 =$	83. $3 \times 3 =$
9. $5 \times 0 =$	34. $8 \times 9 =$	59. $3 \times 5 =$	84. $1 \times 4 =$
10. $3 \times 7 =$	35. $7 \times 5 =$	60. $0 \times 9 =$	85. $8 \times 5 =$
11. $8 \times 2 =$	36. $2 \times 2 =$	61. $5 \times 5 =$	86. $6 \times 6 =$
12. $7 \times 9 =$	37. $3 \times 4 =$	62. $3 \times 9 =$	87. $3 \times 1 =$
13. $3 \times 3 =$	38. $0 \times 10 =$	63. $2 \times 2 =$	88. $3 \times 4 =$
14. $9 \times 9 =$	39. $7 \times 7 =$	64. $4 \times 10 =$	89. $2 \times 8 =$
15. $8 \times 5 =$	40. $4 \times 9 =$	65. $2 \times 6 =$	90. $3 \times 9 =$
16. $3 \times 6 =$	41. $6 \times 6 =$	66. $1 \times 1 =$	91. $4 \times 10 =$
17. $10 \times 5 =$	42. $3 \times 7 =$	67. $3 \times 8 =$	92. $3 \times 6 =$
18. $1 \times 1 =$	43. $2 \times 1 =$	68. $8 \times 8 =$	93. $4 \times 9 =$
19. $6 \times 9 =$	44. $5 \times 3 =$	69. $7 \times 9 =$	94. $5 \times 5 =$
20. $2 \times 3 =$	45. $9 \times 9 =$	70. $7 \times 10 =$	95. $3 \times 8 =$
21. $5 \times 4 =$	46. $3 \times 8 =$	71. $3 \times 7 =$	96. $5 \times 4 =$
22. $3 \times 8 =$	47. $8 \times 9 =$	72. $6 \times 6 =$	97. $1 \times 1 =$
23. $4 \times 4 =$	48. $10 \times 8 =$	73. $9 \times 5 =$	98. $0 \times 4 =$
24. $1 \times 8 =$	49. $1 \times 4 =$	74. $10 \times 7 =$	99. $10 \times 10 =$
25. $3 \times 4 =$	50. $3 \times 9 =$	75. $3 \times 6 =$	100. $2 \times 9 =$

Time?	Time?	Time?	Time?
Did you use strategies?	Where can you improve?	Are you improving?	Did you do well?

Exercise 25A	Exercise 25B	Exercise 25C	Exercise 25D
Name:	Name:	Name:	Name:
Date:	Date:	Date:	Date:
1 $1 \times 4 =$	**26** $4 \times 10 =$	**51** $5 \times 3 =$	**76** $4 \times 4 =$
2 $3 \times 3 =$	**27** $2 \times 2 =$	**52** $4 \times 8 =$	**77** $3 \times 8 =$
3 $4 \times 6 =$	**28** $3 \times 9 =$	**53** $2 \times 1 =$	**78** $4 \times 9 =$
4 $3 \times 9 =$	**29** $5 \times 5 =$	**54** $3 \times 7 =$	**79** $5 \times 4 =$
5 $7 \times 7 =$	**30** $0 \times 9 =$	**55** $6 \times 6 =$	**80** $2 \times 3 =$
6 $3 \times 7 =$	**31** $3 \times 5 =$	**56** $4 \times 7 =$	**81** $6 \times 9 =$
7 $4 \times 7 =$	**32** $4 \times 3 =$	**57** $7 \times 7 =$	**82** $4 \times 6 =$
8 $10 \times 6 =$	**33** $4 \times 4 =$	**58** $0 \times 10 =$	**83** $1 \times 1 =$
9 $8 \times 9 =$	**34** $1 \times 5 =$	**59** $7 \times 9 =$	**84** $10 \times 5 =$
10 $3 \times 5 =$	**35** $3 \times 5 =$	**60** $2 \times 2 =$	**85** $3 \times 6 =$
11 $4 \times 9 =$	**36** $4 \times 8 =$	**61** $4 \times 3 =$	**86** $4 \times 8 =$
12 $5 \times 5 =$	**37** $7 \times 7 =$	**62** $7 \times 5 =$	**87** $8 \times 5 =$
13 $3 \times 6 =$	**38** $6 \times 2 =$	**63** $8 \times 9 =$	**88** $9 \times 9 =$
14 $10 \times 7 =$	**39** $4 \times 7 =$	**64** $3 \times 3 =$	**89** $3 \times 3 =$
15 $4 \times 8 =$	**40** $6 \times 9 =$	**65** $4 \times 6 =$	**90** $4 \times 7 =$
16 $9 \times 5 =$	**41** $3 \times 4 =$	**66** $8 \times 10 =$	**91** $7 \times 9 =$
17 $6 \times 6 =$	**42** $4 \times 5 =$	**67** $5 \times 5 =$	**92** $8 \times 2 =$
18 $3 \times 7 =$	**43** $4 \times 6 =$	**68** $3 \times 6 =$	**93** $3 \times 7 =$
19 $7 \times 10 =$	**44** $3 \times 9 =$	**69** $4 \times 9 =$	**94** $5 \times 0 =$
20 $4 \times 3 =$	**45** $1 \times 4 =$	**70** $9 \times 2 =$	**95** $4 \times 3 =$
21 $7 \times 9 =$	**46** $10 \times 8 =$	**71** $10 \times 10 =$	**96** $3 \times 3 =$
22 $8 \times 8 =$	**47** $4 \times 9 =$	**72** $3 \times 9 =$	**97** $5 \times 6 =$
23 $3 \times 8 =$	**48** $8 \times 3 =$	**73** $3 \times 5 =$	**98** $8 \times 5 =$
24 $1 \times 1 =$	**49** $8 \times 9 =$	**74** $3 \times 4 =$	**99** $3 \times 5 =$
25 $2 \times 6 =$	**50** $9 \times 9 =$	**75** $1 \times 8 =$	**100** $6 \times 9 =$
Time?	Time?	Time?	Time?

How did you do?

Did you beat your best score?

Can you try to be faster?

Have you reached your target?

Exercise 26A	Exercise 26B	Exercise 26C	Exercise 26D
Name:	Name:	Name:	Name:
Date:	Date:	Date:	Date:

Exercise 26A	Exercise 26B	Exercise 26C	Exercise 26D
1. $1 \times 1 =$	26. $8 \times 5 =$	51. $4 \times 6 =$	76. $4 \times 3 =$
2. $6 \times 7 =$	27. $3 \times 6 =$	52. $3 \times 4 =$	77. $5 \times 0 =$
3. $1 \times 8 =$	28. $4 \times 8 =$	53. $6 \times 9 =$	78. $4 \times 7 =$
4. $3 \times 4 =$	29. $10 \times 5 =$	54. $4 \times 7 =$	79. $3 \times 7 =$
5. $6 \times 9 =$	30. $1 \times 1 =$	55. $6 \times 7 =$	80. $8 \times 2 =$
6. $3 \times 5 =$	31. $4 \times 6 =$	56. $6 \times 2 =$	81. $7 \times 9 =$
7. $8 \times 5 =$	32. $6 \times 9 =$	57. $7 \times 7 =$	82. $4 \times 7 =$
8. $5 \times 6 =$	33. $6 \times 8 =$	58. $4 \times 8 =$	83. $3 \times 3 =$
9. $6 \times 8 =$	34. $2 \times 3 =$	59. $3 \times 5 =$	84. $6 \times 7 =$
10. $3 \times 3 =$	35. $5 \times 4 =$	60. $1 \times 5 =$	85. $9 \times 9 =$
11. $4 \times 3 =$	36. $4 \times 9 =$	61. $4 \times 4 =$	86. $8 \times 5 =$
12. $5 \times 0 =$	37. $3 \times 8 =$	62. $4 \times 3 =$	87. $4 \times 8 =$
13. $3 \times 7 =$	38. $4 \times 4 =$	63. $4 \times 9 =$	88. $3 \times 6 =$
14. $8 \times 2 =$	39. $1 \times 8 =$	64. $3 \times 5 =$	89. $6 \times 8 =$
15. $7 \times 9 =$	40. $3 \times 4 =$	65. $0 \times 9 =$	90. $1 \times 1 =$
16. $6 \times 9 =$	41. $6 \times 7 =$	66. $6 \times 9 =$	91. $4 \times 6 =$
17. $4 \times 7 =$	42. $3 \times 5 =$	67. $5 \times 5 =$	92. $0 \times 8 =$
18. $3 \times 3 =$	43. $3 \times 9 =$	68. $3 \times 9 =$	93. $1 \times 7 =$
19. $9 \times 9 =$	44. $10 \times 10 =$	69. $2 \times 2 =$	94. $5 \times 4 =$
20. $8 \times 5 =$	45. $9 \times 2 =$	70. $4 \times 10 =$	95. $3 \times 8 =$
21. $4 \times 8 =$	46. $3 \times 6 =$	71. $2 \times 1 =$	96. $6 \times 9 =$
22. $3 \times 6 =$	47. $5 \times 5 =$	72. $6 \times 8 =$	97. $4 \times 4 =$
23. $10 \times 5 =$	48. $8 \times 10 =$	73. $3 \times 8 =$	98. $1 \times 8 =$
24. $1 \times 1 =$	49. $4 \times 6 =$	74. $7 \times 9 =$	99. $3 \times 6 =$
25. $4 \times 6 =$	50. $6 \times 9 =$	75. $8 \times 8 =$	100. $3 \times 4 =$

Exercise 26A	Exercise 26B	Exercise 26C	Exercise 26D
Time?	Time?	Time?	Time?
How do you think you are doing?	How did you do?	Is this your best score?	Which facts do you find the easiest?

Exercise 27A	Exercise 27B	Exercise 27C	Exercise 27D
Name:	Name:	Name:	Name:
Date:	Date:	Date:	Date:
1 8 x 2 =	26 8 x 8 =	51 6 x 2 =	76 3 x 8 =
2 7 x 9 =	27 4 x 7 =	52 6 x 7 =	77 4 x 9 =
3 3 x 7 =	28 7 x 9 =	53 5 x 7 =	78 5 x 4 =
4 3 x 3 =	29 7 x 8 =	54 4 x 7 =	79 4 x 7 =
5 6 x 7 =	30 3 x 8 =	55 6 x 9 =	80 2 x 3 =
6 9 x 9 =	31 6 x 8 =	56 3 x 4 =	81 6 x 8 =
7 7 x 8 =	32 3 x 7 =	57 4 x 6 =	82 6 x 9 =
8 4 x 7 =	33 2 x 1 =	58 9 x 7 =	83 7 x 7 =
9 8 x 5 =	34 4 x 10 =	59 6 x 9 =	84 4 x 6 =
10 4 x 8 =	35 2 x 2 =	60 4 x 6 =	85 1 x 1 =
11 3 x 6 =	36 3 x 9 =	61 8 x 10 =	86 10 x 5 =
12 6 x 8 =	37 5 x 5 =	62 8 x 7 =	87 4 x 8 =
13 8 x 7 =	38 6 x 9 =	63 5 x 5 =	88 0 x 6 =
14 1 x 1 =	39 9 x 7 =	64 1 x 8 =	89 8 x 7 =
15 4 x 6 =	40 0 x 9 =	65 3 x 6 =	90 3 x 6 =
16 0 x 8 =	41 3 x 5 =	66 6 x 7 =	91 8 x 5 =
17 1 x 7 =	42 4 x 9 =	67 9 x 2 =	92 4 x 6 =
18 6 x 7 =	43 4 x 3 =	68 10 x 10 =	93 1 x 1 =
19 5 x 4 =	44 4 x 4 =	69 3 x 9 =	94 9 x 7 =
20 3 x 8 =	45 8 x 7 =	70 3 x 5 =	95 10 x 5 =
21 6 x 9 =	46 1 x 5 =	71 8 x 7 =	96 3 x 6 =
22 9 x 7 =	47 3 x 5 =	72 6 x 7 =	97 4 x 8 =
23 4 x 4 =	48 4 x 8 =	73 3 x 4 =	98 8 x 5 =
24 1 x 8 =	49 7 x 7 =	74 1 x 8 =	99 9 x 9 =
25 3 x 6 =	50 6 x 7 =	75 4 x 4 =	100 3 x 3 =
Time?	Time?	Time?	Time?

Did you do well?

What have you learnt today?

Have you reached your target?

What is your time?

Exercise 28A

Name:

Date:

1. $2 \times \square = 14$
2. $\square \times 10 = 80$
3. $10 \times \square = 40$
4. $8 \times \square = 80$
5. $\square \times 7 = 14$
6. $8 \times \square = 16$
7. $\square \times 10 = 100$
8. $7 \times \square = 14$
9. $10 \times \square = 10$
10. $\square \times 2 = 8$
11. $10 \times \square = 0$
12. $\square \times 9 = 90$
13. $2 \times \square = 16$
14. $\square \times 7 = 70$
15. $6 \times \square = 12$
16. $10 \times \square = 100$
17. $\square \times 5 = 50$
18. $2 \times \square = 8$
19. $\square \times 8 = 80$
20. $\square \times 2 = 20$
21. $1 \times \square = 10$
22. $\square \times 3 = 6$
23. $3 \times \square = 30$
24. $\square \times 2 = 18$
25. $10 \times \square = 60$

Exercise 28B

Name:

Date:

26. $8 \times \square = 16$
27. $\square \times 10 = 0$
28. $2 \times \square = 14$
29. $\square \times 4 = 40$
30. $1 \times \square = 2$
31. $1 \times \square = 10$
32. $\square \times 8 = 80$
33. $2 \times \square = 8$
34. $\square \times 2 = 14$
35. $2 \times \square = 20$
36. $\square \times 10 = 90$
37. $1 \times \square = 10$
38. $2 \times \square = 6$
39. $\square \times 10 = 30$
40. $9 \times \square = 18$
41. $\square \times 6 = 60$
42. $2 \times \square = 4$
43. $8 \times \square = 16$
44. $\square \times 10 = 0$
45. $2 \times \square = 14$
46. $\square \times 4 = 40$
47. $1 \times \square = 2$
48. $1 \times \square = 10$
49. $\square \times 8 = 80$
50. $2 \times \square = 8$

Exercise 28C

Name:

Date:

51. $10 \times \square = 40$
52. $\square \times 3 = 6$
53. $8 \times \square = 80$
54. $5 \times \square = 10$
55. $7 \times \square = 70$
56. $\square \times 3 = 30$
57. $2 \times \square = 4$
58. $\square \times 10 = 20$
59. $8 \times \square = 16$
60. $\square \times 6 = 60$
61. $2 \times \square = 8$
62. $2 \times \square = 20$
63. $\square \times 2 = 2$
64. $10 \times \square = 90$
65. $\square \times 10 = 50$
66. $2 \times \square = 12$
67. $\square \times 1 = 10$
68. $7 \times \square = 14$
69. $2 \times \square = 16$
70. $\square \times 8 = 16$
71. $7 \times \square = 70$
72. $\square \times 2 = 20$
73. $10 \times \square = 100$
74. $\square \times 8 = 16$
75. $10 \times \square = 0$

Exercise 28D

Name:

Date:

76. $7 \times \square = 70$
77. $\square \times 2 = 18$
78. $10 \times \square = 70$
79. $2 \times \square = 16$
80. $\square \times 10 = 40$
81. $10 \times \square = 80$
82. $\square \times 2 = 8$
83. $10 \times \square = 100$
84. $\square \times 3 = 6$
85. $10 \times \square = 50$
86. $\square \times 2 = 12$
87. $8 \times \square = 80$
88. $\square \times 2 = 4$
89. $10 \times \square = 40$
90. $\square \times 10 = 70$
91. $9 \times \square = 90$
92. $\square \times 2 = 2$
93. $\square \times 6 = 60$
94. $10 \times \square = 70$
95. $\square \times 4 = 40$
96. $9 \times \square = 90$
97. $10 \times \square = 60$
98. $\square \times 3 = 30$
99. $9 \times \square = 18$
100. $\square \times 2 = 16$

Time? — Try to be even quicker next time?

Time? — How are you doing?

Time? — Try to be faster?

Time? — Did you beat your target?

Exercise 29A	Exercise 29B	Exercise 29C	Exercise 29D

Name: ___   Date: ___ | Name: ___   Date: ___ | Name: ___   Date: ___ | Name: ___   Date: ___

Exercise 29 (2 Tables) Missing Box x10, x5

#	Exercise 29A	#	Exercise 29B	#	Exercise 29C	#	Exercise 29D
1	10 x □ = 80	26	10 x □ = 20	51	□ x 5 = 25	76	□ x 9 = 45
2	□ x 10 = 20	27	□ x 5 = 30	52	6 x □ = 60	77	10 x □ = 80
3	8 x □ = 40	28	4 x □ = 20	53	□ x 5 = 45	78	□ x 1 = 10
4	□ x 7 = 70	29	□ x 10 = 70	54	10 x □ = 90	79	4 x □ = 20
5	5 x □ = 20	30	10 x □ = 50	55	5 x □ = 30	80	5 x □ = 50
6	5 x □ = 50	31	□ x 3 = 30	56	□ x 10 = 30	81	□ x 8 = 40
7	□ x 5 = 35	32	□ x 5 = 25	57	7 x □ = 35	82	10 x □ = 100
8	10 x □ = 10	33	9 x □ = 90	58	□ x 10 = 100	83	□ x 5 = 25
9	□ x 8 = 80	34	□ x 5 = 5	59	2 x □ = 10	84	6 x □ = 60
10	5 x □ = 30	35	10 x □ = 80	60	□ x 10 = 30	85	□ x 1 = 5
11	□ x 5 = 25	36	□ x 6 = 30	61	4 x □ = 20	86	10 x □ = 50
12	6 x □ = 60	37	10 x □ = 100	62	□ x 1 = 10	87	□ x 1 = 10
13	□ x 5 = 45	38	□ x 5 = 35	63	5 x □ = 25	88	□ x 7 = 70
14	10 x □ = 90	39	10 x □ = 40	64	7 x □ = 70	89	5 x □ = 20
15	□ x 6 = 30	40	□ x 2 = 10	65	□ x 10 = 90	90	□ x 10 = 50
16	3 x □ = 30	41	10 x □ = 50	66	2 x □ = 10	91	7 x □ = 35
17	7 x □ = 35	42	□ x 5 = 35	67	□ x 5 = 50	92	□ x 1 = 10
18	□ x 10 = 100	43	9 x □ = 90	68	5 x □ = 30	93	8 x □ = 80
19	6 x □ = 60	44	□ x 7 = 70	69	□ x 10 = 50	94	□ x 6 = 30
20	□ x 8 = 40	45	5 x □ = 20	70	7 x □ = 35	95	5 x □ = 25
21	10 x □ = 100	46	5 x □ = 50	71	□ x 4 = 40	96	□ x 10 = 60
22	3 x □ = 15	47	□ x 5 = 35	72	3 x □ = 15	97	9 x □ = 45
23	□ x 10 = 80	48	10 x □ = 10	73	□ x 10 = 0	98	10 x □ = 90
24	1 x □ = 10	49	□ x 8 = 80	74	7 x □ = 35	99	□ x 6 = 30
25	□ x 9 = 45	50	5 x □ = 30	75	□ x 10 = 60	100	3 x □ = 30

Time? | Time? | Time? | Time?

Which facts did you find the hardest? | Did you beat your target? | Can you try to be faster? | Where do you need to improve?

Exercise 30 (2 Tables) Missing Box x2, x5

Exercise 30A	Exercise 30B	Exercise 30C	Exercise 30D
Name:	Name:	Name:	Name:
Date:	Date:	Date:	Date:

1 ☐ x 2 = 0   **26** 10 x ☐ = 20   **51** ☐ x 2 = 2   **76** ☐ x 7 = 35

2 5 x ☐ = 20   **27** ☐ x 5 = 45   **52** 10 x ☐ = 50   **77** 5 x ☐ = 10

3 2 x ☐ = 10   **28** 2 x ☐ = 12   **53** ☐ x 5 = 0   **78** ☐ x 2 = 20

4 ☐ x 5 = 35   **29** 8 x ☐ = 40   **54** 5 x ☐ = 30   **79** 9 x ☐ = 45

5 2 x ☐ = 2   **30** ☐ x 5 = 0   **55** 5 x ☐ = 20   **80** 2 x ☐ = 12

6 5 x ☐ = 30   **31** 5 x ☐ = 20   **56** ☐ x 5 = 35   **81** ☐ x 5 = 40

7 ☐ x 2 = 18   **32** ☐ x 4 = 8   **57** 2 x ☐ = 2   **82** 2 x ☐ = 0

8 8 x ☐ = 40   **33** 10 x ☐ = 50   **58** ☐ x 6 = 30   **83** ☐ x 4 = 20

9 ☐ x 2 = 12   **34** 7 x ☐ = 14   **59** 9 x ☐ = 18   **84** 2 x ☐ = 8

10 4 x ☐ = 20   **35** ☐ x 5 = 25   **60** ☐ x 5 = 40   **85** 10 x ☐ = 50

11 2 x ☐ = 4   **36** 1 x ☐ = 2   **61** 6 x ☐ = 12   **86** ☐ x 2 = 14

12 ☐ x 10 = 20   **37** ☐ x 5 = 45   **62** 4 x ☐ = 20   **87** 5 x ☐ = 25

13 5 x ☐ = 25   **38** 2 x ☐ = 0   **63** ☐ x 2 = 4   **88** ☐ x 2 = 2

14 ☐ x 9 = 45   **39** 5 x ☐ = 10   **64** 2 x ☐ = 20   **89** ☐ x 5 = 45

15 2 x ☐ = 0   **40** ☐ x 6 = 30   **65** ☐ x 5 = 25   **90** 5 x ☐ = 0

16 ☐ x 5 = 30   **41** 2 x ☐ = 4   **66** 5 x ☐ = 45   **91** ☐ x 2 = 10

17 2 x ☐ = 6   **42** ☐ x 5 = 5   **67** ☐ x 2 = 0   **92** 2 x ☐ = 4

18 ☐ x 10 = 50   **43** 8 x ☐ = 16   **68** 6 x ☐ = 30   **93** ☐ x 5 = 5

19 7 x ☐ = 14   **44** 5 x ☐ = 35   **69** ☐ x 3 = 6   **94** 8 x ☐ = 16

20 ☐ x 5 = 40   **45** ☐ x 2 = 6   **70** 5 x ☐ = 50   **95** ☐ x 7 = 35

21 4 x ☐ = 8   **46** 4 x ☐ = 8   **71** ☐ x 2 = 14   **96** 3 x ☐ = 6

22 ☐ x 5 = 40   **47** ☐ x 2 = 12   **72** 8 x ☐ = 40   **97** ☐ x 2 = 14

23 2 x ☐ = 18   **48** 5 x ☐ = 40   **73** ☐ x 2 = 8   **98** 5 x ☐ = 35

24 5 x ☐ = 35   **49** ☐ x 2 = 14   **74** 8 x ☐ = 16   **99** ☐ x 2 = 2

25 ☐ x 2 = 10   **50** 3 x ☐ = 15   **75** 2 x ☐ = 18   **100** 4 x ☐ = 20

Time?	Time?	Time?	Time?

Is this your best score?   Have you reached your target?   Did you do well?   Do you think you are improving?

Exercise 31A	Exercise 31B	Exercise 31C	Exercise 31D
Name:	Name:	Name:	Name:
Date:	Date:	Date:	Date:

1 9 x ☐ = 18   **26** 9 x ☐ = 27   **51** 9 x ☐ = 81   **76** ☐ x 3 = 27

2 ☐ x 3 = 9   **27** ☐ x 5 = 25   **52** ☐ x 5 = 25   **77** ☐ x 1 = 1

3 8 x ☐ = 72   **28** 6 x ☐ = 54   **53** 7 x ☐ = 49   **78** 0 x ☐ = 0

4 4 x ☐ = 16   **29** ☐ x 10 = 100   **54** 2 x ☐ = 18   **79** ☐ x 9 = 63

5 ☐ x 1 = 9   **30** 9 x ☐ = 72   **55** ☐ x 2 = 4   **80** 4 x ☐ = 16

6 9 x ☐ = 0   **31** ☐ x 1 = 1   **56** 3 x ☐ = 27   **81** ☐ x 2 = 18

7 ☐ x 9 = 81   **32** 6 x ☐ = 36   **57** ☐ x 6 = 36   **82** 3 x ☐ = 9

8 6 x ☐ = 36   **33** ☐ x 9 = 63   **58** 9 x ☐ = 72   **83** 7 x ☐ = 49

9 ☐ x 3 = 27   **34** 8 x ☐ = 64   **59** ☐ x 1 = 1   **84** ☐ x 9 = 72

10 2 x ☐ = 4   **35** 9 x ☐ = 81   **60** 4 x ☐ = 36   **85** 5 x ☐ = 25

11 ☐ x 9 = 90   **36** ☐ x 3 = 9   **61** ☐ x 0 = 0   **86** ☐ x 7 = 49

12 7 x ☐ = 49   **37** 7 x ☐ = 49   **62** ☐ x 8 = 64   **87** 4 x ☐ = 36

13 9 x ☐ = 0   **38** ☐ x 10 = 90   **63** 4 x ☐ = 36   **88** ☐ x 6 = 36

14 ☐ x 9 = 81   **39** 4 x ☐ = 16   **64** ☐ x 6 = 36   **89** 3 x ☐ = 27

15 ☐ x 10 = 100   **40** ☐ x 9 = 72   **65** 9 x ☐ = 81   **90** 1 x ☐ = 1

16 3 x ☐ = 9   **41** 7 x ☐ = 49   **66** ☐ x 1 = 1   **91** ☐ x 7 = 63

17 ☐ x 0 = 0   **42** ☐ x 9 = 54   **67** 9 x ☐ = 45   **92** 2 x ☐ = 4

18 9 x ☐ = 36   **43** 8 x ☐ = 64   **68** ☐ x 10 = 100   **93** ☐ x 9 = 45

19 ☐ x 6 = 36   **44** ☐ x 9 = 0   **69** 10 x ☐ = 90   **94** 7 x ☐ = 49

20 3 x ☐ = 27   **45** 6 x ☐ = 36   **70** 5 x ☐ = 25   **95** ☐ x 3 = 27

21 1 x ☐ = 1   **46** 9 x ☐ = 90   **71** ☐ x 4 = 36   **96** 5 x ☐ = 25

22 ☐ x 7 = 63   **47** ☐ x 9 = 63   **72** 7 x ☐ = 49   **97** ☐ x 9 = 54

23 2 x ☐ = 4   **48** 1 x ☐ = 1   **73** ☐ x 2 = 4   **98** 10 x ☐ = 100

24 ☐ x 9 = 45   **49** ☐ x 1 = 9   **74** 6 x ☐ = 54   **99** ☐ x 8 = 72

25 7 x ☐ = 49   **50** 10 x ☐ = 100   **75** ☐ x 6 = 36   **100** 1 x ☐ = 1

Time?   Time?   Time?   Time?

Try to concentrate even more!

How do you think you are doing?

What have you learnt today?

How could you recall these facts even quicker

Exercise 32A	Exercise 32B	Exercise 32C	Exercise 32D
Name:	Name:	Name:	Name:
Date:	Date:	Date:	Date:

1 10 x ☐ = 40	**26** ☐ x 3 = 30	**51** 3 x ☐ = 6	**76** 9 x ☐ = 36
2 ☐ x 3 = 9	**27** 4 x ☐ = 12	**52** ☐ x 4 = 0	**77** ☐ x 6 = 18
3 ☐ x 4 = 8	**28** ☐ x 3 = 0	**53** 3 x ☐ = 9	**78** 9 x ☐ = 27
4 3 x ☐ = 0	**29** 7 x ☐ = 21	**54** ☐ x 4 = 16	**79** 7 x ☐ = 28
5 ☐ x 4 = 36	**30** ☐ x 4 = 16	**55** ☐ x 10 = 30	**80** ☐ x 3 = 21
6 3 x ☐ = 18	**31** ☐ x 4 = 0	**56** 8 x ☐ = 32	**81** 4 x ☐ = 0
7 ☐ x 3 = 27	**32** 4 x ☐ = 36	**57** 3 x ☐ = 0	**82** ☐ x 2 = 6
8 7 x ☐ = 28	**33** ☐ x 3 = 3	**58** ☐ x 3 = 15	**83** 5 x ☐ = 20
9 ☐ x 3 = 21	**34** 5 x ☐ = 20	**59** 4 x ☐ = 36	**84** 8 x ☐ = 24
10 4 x ☐ = 0	**35** ☐ x 8 = 24	**60** ☐ x 3 = 9	**85** ☐ x 1 = 4
11 ☐ x 2 = 6	**36** 4 x ☐ = 40	**61** 6 x ☐ = 24	**86** 3 x ☐ = 30
12 5 x ☐ = 20	**37** ☐ x 3 = 3	**62** ☐ x 3 = 0	**87** ☐ x 4 = 32
13 8 x ☐ = 24	**38** 6 x ☐ = 24	**63** 4 x ☐ = 40	**88** 1 x ☐ = 3
14 ☐ x 1 = 4	**39** ☐ x 3 = 12	**64** ☐ x 6 = 18	**89** ☐ x 4 = 40
15 3 x ☐ = 30	**40** 3 x ☐ = 0	**65** 1 x ☐ = 3	**90** 3 x ☐ = 9
16 ☐ x 4 = 32	**41** ☐ x 3 = 21	**66** 5 x ☐ = 20	**91** 2 x ☐ = 8
17 1 x ☐ = 3	**42** 4 x ☐ = 16	**67** ☐ x 1 = 3	**92** ☐ x 3 = 0
18 6 x ☐ = 18	**43** ☐ x 4 = 0	**68** 7 x ☐ = 21	**93** 4 x ☐ = 12
19 ☐ x 4 = 16	**44** 4 x ☐ = 36	**69** ☐ x 4 = 0	**94** ☐ x 3 = 18
20 4 x ☐ = 12	**45** ☐ x 3 = 3	**70** 3 x ☐ = 6	**95** 4 x ☐ = 16
21 ☐ x 3 = 15	**46** 5 x ☐ = 20	**71** ☐ x 4 = 16	**96** ☐ x 3 = 12
22 2 x ☐ = 6	**47** 3 x ☐ = 24	**72** 3 x ☐ = 24	**97** 3 x ☐ = 27
23 ☐ x 2 = 8	**48** ☐ x 10 = 40	**73** ☐ x 1 = 4	**98** 7 x ☐ = 28
24 3 x ☐ = 18	**49** 1 x ☐ = 3	**74** 3 x ☐ = 9	**99** ☐ x 3 = 15
25 ☐ x 4 = 32	**50** ☐ x 4 = 24	**75** 9 x ☐ = 27	**100** ☐ x 3 = 6

Time?	Time?	Time?	Time?
Are the facts at your fingertips?	Try to really focus!	Which facts do you find the easiest?	Did you do well?

Exercise 33A	Exercise 33B	Exercise 33C	Exercise 33D
Name:	Name:	Name:	Name:
Date:	Date:	Date:	Date:

1 4 x □ = 28	**26** 9 x □ = 63	**51** 6 x □ = 42	**76** 6 x □ = 0
2 □ x 6 = 6	**27** □ x 6 = 0	**52** □ x 4 = 28	**77** □ x 8 = 56
3 7 x □ = 56	**28** 10 x □ = 70	**53** 1 x □ = 6	**78** 1 x □ = 6
4 □ x 7 = 42	**29** □ x 10 = 60	**54** 6 x □ = 42	**79** □ x 7 = 14
5 □ x 5 = 35	**30** □ x 7 = 28	**55** □ x 8 = 48	**80** 6 x □ = 36
6 2 x □ = 12	**31** 1 x □ = 6	**56** 7 x □ = 0	**81** □ x 7 = 49
7 7 x □ = 0	**32** □ x 7 = 42	**57** □ x 6 = 12	**82** □ x 6 = 42
8 □ x 8 = 48	**33** 7 x □ = 0	**58** □ x 7 = 49	**83** 6 x □ = 60
9 3 x □ = 18	**34** □ x 6 = 24	**59** 6 x □ = 54	**84** □ x 6 = 48
10 □ x 9 = 63	**35** 5 x □ = 35	**60** 7 x □ = 7	**85** 3 x □ = 21
11 6 x □ = 0	**36** □ x 2 = 12	**61** □ x 6 = 18	**86** □ x 6 = 12
12 1 x □ = 7	**37** 7 x □ = 7	**62** 8 x □ = 56	**87** 7 x □ = 21
13 □ x 6 = 24	**38** 8 x □ = 48	**63** □ x 10 = 60	**88** 9 x □ = 54
14 7 x □ = 70	**39** □ x 5 = 30	**64** 6 x □ = 0	**89** □ x 8 = 48
15 □ x 1 = 6	**40** 2 x □ = 14	**65** □ x 2 = 14	**90** □ x 6 = 18
16 4 x □ = 28	**41** □ x 6 = 18	**66** □ x 4 = 24	**91** 7 x □ = 63
17 □ x 2 = 14	**42** 7 x □ = 42	**67** 7 x □ = 63	**92** □ x 7 = 7
18 5 x □ = 30	**43** □ x 4 = 24	**68** 1 x □ = 6	**93** 4 x □ = 24
19 6 x □ = 42	**44** 7 x □ = 49	**69** □ x 3 = 21	**94** □ x 10 = 70
20 □ x 9 = 54	**45** □ x 6 = 30	**70** 6 x □ = 6	**95** 6 x □ = 6
21 5 x □ = 30	**46** 7 x □ = 28	**71** □ x 6 = 24	**96** □ x 7 = 28
22 □ x 8 = 56	**47** □ x 6 = 36	**72** 6 x □ = 42	**97** 7 x □ = 14
23 □ x 9 = 54	**48** 10 x □ = 70	**73** □ x 6 = 0	**98** □ x 6 = 30
24 3 x □ = 21	**49** □ x 6 = 0	**74** 7 x □ = 14	**99** 6 x □ = 42
25 □ x 6 = 42	**50** 5 x □ = 35	**75** □ x 6 = 30	**100** 6 x □ = 54

Time?	Time?	Time?	Time?

Did you beat you score?

Which facts do you find the hardest?

Is this your best score?

Try to concentrate even more?

Exercise 34A	Exercise 34B	Exercise 34C	Exercise 34D
Name:	Name:	Name:	Name:
Date:	Date:	Date:	Date:

#	34A	#	34B	#	34C	#	34D
1	6 x □ = 48	26	3 x □ = 21	51	8 x □ = 64	76	4 x □ = 32
2	□ x 4 = 32	27	□ x 8 = 32	52	□ x 8 = 0	77	□ x 7 = 7
3	□ x 7 = 21	28	7 x □ = 49	53	2 x □ = 16	78	8 x □ = 64
4	7 x □ = 63	29	8 x □ = 80	54	5 x □ = 35	79	□ x 8 = 40
5	□ x 8 = 0	30	□ x 8 = 72	55	□ x 9 = 72	80	6 x □ = 42
6	4 x □ = 28	31	4 x □ = 28	56	8 x □ = 56	81	□ x 8 = 0
7	□ x 7 = 56	32	□ x 7 = 0	57	□ x 8 = 24	82	1 x □ = 7
8	7 x □ = 70	33	8 x □ = 24	58	6 x □ = 42	83	□ x 8 = 72
9	□ x 8 = 8	34	□ x 9 = 63	59	7 x □ = 7	84	7 x □ = 49
10	4 x □ = 28	35	□ x 8 = 64	60	□ x 8 = 32	85	□ x 8 = 48
11	□ x 8 = 64	36	5 x □ = 35	61	7 x □ = 49	86	2 x □ = 14
12	7 x □ = 0	37	2 x □ = 14	62	5 x □ = 35	87	□ x 1 = 8
13	□ x 8 = 16	38	□ x 5 = 40	63	□ x 8 = 64	88	8 x □ = 56
14	5 x □ = 35	39	8 x □ = 80	64	7 x □ = 63	89	10 x □ = 80
15	□ x 9 = 72	40	□ x 8 = 56	65	□ x 3 = 24	90	□ x 3 = 21
16	□ x 7 = 56	41	6 x □ = 48	66	7 x □ = 0	91	2 x □ = 16
17	3 x □ = 24	42	□ x 4 = 32	67	□ x 8 = 8	92	□ x 7 = 14
18	□ x 7 = 42	43	3 x □ = 21	68	4 x □ = 28	93	8 x □ = 40
19	7 x □ = 7	44	□ x 9 = 63	69	9 x □ = 72	94	10 x □ = 80
20	□ x 8 = 32	45	8 x □ = 0	70	□ x 10 = 80	95	□ x 8 = 56
21	9 x □ = 81	46	□ x 7 = 28	71	7 x □ = 7	96	6 x □ = 48
22	□ x 4 = 28	47	7 x □ = 56	72	4 x □ = 32	97	□ x 4 = 32
23	□ x 2 = 16	48	□ x 10 = 70	73	□ x 7 = 42	98	3 x □ = 21
24	8 x □ = 56	49	1 x □ = 8	74	8 x □ = 0	99	□ x 9 = 63
25	□ x 7 = 0	50	4 x □ = 28	75	7 x □ = 70	100	□ x 8 = 0

Time?	Time?	Time?	Time?
Is this your best score yet?	Did you beat your target?	Have you reached your target yet?	How do you think you are doing?

Exercise 35A	Exercise 35B	Exercise 35C	Exercise 35D
Name:	Name:	Name:	Name:
Date:	Date:	Date:	Date:

Exercise 35A

1. $10 \times \square = 70$
2. $\square \times 4 = 4$
3. $3 \times \square = 0$
4. $4 \times \square = 40$
5. $\square \times 3 = 3$
6. $6 \times \square = 6$
7. $\square \times 10 = 30$
8. $\square \times 8 = 0$
9. $4 \times \square = 0$
10. $2 \times \square = 20$
11. $\square \times 7 = 7$
12. $10 \times \square = 90$
13. $\square \times 3 = 3$
14. $5 \times \square = 50$
15. $\square \times 4 = 0$
16. $10 \times \square = 20$
17. $5 \times \square = 0$
18. $\square \times 1 = 8$
19. $7 \times \square = 70$
20. $\square \times 7 = 0$
21. $\square \times 8 = 8$
22. $10 \times \square = 60$
23. $6 \times \square = 6$
24. $\square \times 4 = 40$
25. $1 \times \square = 9$

Exercise 35B

26. $5 \times \square = 0$
27. $\square \times 10 = 50$
28. $\square \times 10 = 0$
29. $\square \times 8 = 8$
30. $1 \times \square = 9$
31. $10 \times \square = 90$
32. $\square \times 1 = 0$
33. $8 \times \square = 80$
34. $\square \times 10 = 0$
35. $10 \times \square = 100$
36. $2 \times \square = 2$
37. $\square \times 7 = 70$
38. $1 \times \square = 10$
39. $\square \times 4 = 4$
40. $6 \times \square = 0$
41. $1 \times \square = 10$
42. $\square \times 2 = 2$
43. $3 \times \square = 0$
44. $\square \times 7 = 7$
45. $\square \times 1 = 0$
46. $1 \times \square = 10$
47. $1 \times \square = 6$
48. $\square \times 10 = 70$
49. $10 \times \square = 90$
50. $3 \times \square = 0$

Exercise 35C

51. $\square \times 6 = 0$
52. $1 \times \square = 7$
53. $\square \times 1 = 8$
54. $\square \times 3 = 0$
55. $10 \times \square = 70$
56. $1 \times \square = 6$
57. $\square \times 10 = 60$
58. $1 \times \square = 0$
59. $\square \times 1 = 7$
60. $10 \times \square = 40$
61. $\square \times 5 = 0$
62. $1 \times \square = 8$
63. $\square \times 10 = 60$
64. $\square \times 10 = 30$
65. $4 \times \square = 0$
66. $\square \times 1 = 6$
67. $10 \times \square = 90$
68. $9 \times \square = 9$
69. $1 \times \square = 10$
70. $10 \times \square = 100$
71. $8 \times \square = 0$
72. $1 \times \square = 7$
73. $3 \times \square = 0$
74. $10 \times \square = 70$
75. $1 \times \square = 4$

Exercise 35D

76. $\square \times 4 = 0$
77. $1 \times \square = 7$
78. $\square \times 6 = 0$
79. $10 \times \square = 20$
80. $\square \times 10 = 100$
81. $8 \times \square = 0$
82. $10 \times \square = 70$
83. $\square \times 2 = 0$
84. $1 \times \square = 6$
85. $\square \times 10 = 70$
86. $\square \times 7 = 0$
87. $10 \times \square = 80$
88. $9 \times \square = 0$
89. $\square \times 1 = 7$
90. $10 \times \square = 40$
91. $\square \times 8 = 0$
92. $10 \times \square = 80$
93. $\square \times 1 = 9$
94. $10 \times \square = 30$
95. $\square \times 5 = 0$
96. $1 \times \square = 6$
97. $\square \times 2 = 0$
98. $10 \times \square = 50$
99. $\square \times 1 = 5$
100. $7 \times \square = 0$

Time?	Time?	Time?	Time?

Try to be even quicker next time!

Can you try to be faster?

Did you do well?

What have you learnt today?

Exercise 36A	Exercise 36B	Exercise 36C	Exercise 36D
Name:	Name:	Name:	Name:
Date:	Date:	Date:	Date:

#	36A	#	36B	#	36C	#	36D
1	☐ x 3 = 30	26	☐ x 0 = 0	51	☐ x 3 = 0	76	☐ x 3 = 6
2	2 x ☐ = 6	27	8 x ☐ = 16	52	10 x ☐ = 40	77	10 x ☐ = 80
3	10 x ☐ = 80	28	10 x ☐ = 50	53	☐ x 6 = 6	78	1 x ☐ = 4
4	☐ x 4 = 4	29	☐ x 10 = 100	54	4 x ☐ = 8	79	☐ x 2 = 12
5	6 x ☐ = 12	30	☐ x 3 = 6	55	☐ x 10 = 40	80	5 x ☐ = 5
6	☐ x 1 = 5	31	1 x ☐ = 9	56	2 x ☐ = 0	81	☐ x 9 = 0
7	0 x ☐ = 0	32	☐ x 2 = 18	57	☐ x 10 = 90	82	4 x ☐ = 40
8	☐ x 10 = 40	33	8 x ☐ = 80	58	4 x ☐ = 8	83	☐ x 7 = 14
9	☐ x 7 = 14	34	☐ x 10 = 0	59	3 x ☐ = 0	84	10 x ☐ = 70
10	10 x ☐ = 70	35	2 x ☐ = 2	60	☐ x 8 = 80	85	☐ x 1 = 1
11	☐ x 1 = 1	36	☐ x 5 = 10	61	1 x ☐ = 4	86	9 x ☐ = 18
12	9 x ☐ = 18	37	7 x ☐ = 7	62	☐ x 7 = 14	87	☐ x 4 = 0
13	☐ x 4 = 0	38	☐ x 6 = 0	63	☐ x 1 = 5	88	4 x ☐ = 40
14	4 x ☐ = 40	39	☐ x 10 = 40	64	9 x ☐ = 0	89	☐ x 8 = 16
15	☐ x 8 = 16	40	4 x ☐ = 8	65	☐ x 2 = 10	90	3 x ☐ = 3
16	3 x ☐ = 3	41	☐ x 1 = 3	66	10 x ☐ = 70	91	☐ x 4 = 4
17	☐ x 4 = 4	42	0 x ☐ = 0	67	☐ x 1 = 3	92	10 x ☐ = 60
18	10 x ☐ = 60	43	☐ x 10 = 20	68	8 x ☐ = 16	93	5 x ☐ = 10
19	☐ x 2 = 10	44	2 x ☐ = 12	69	☐ x 6 = 6	94	☐ x 2 = 14
20	7 x ☐ = 14	45	☐ x 10 = 70	70	6 x ☐ = 0	95	6 x ☐ = 60
21	☐ x 6 = 60	46	2 x ☐ = 4	71	3 x ☐ = 6	96	1 x ☐ = 8
22	1 x ☐ = 8	47	0 x ☐ = 0	72	☐ x 9 = 90	97	☐ x 2 = 4
23	☐ x 2 = 4	48	☐ x 10 = 80	73	4 x ☐ = 0	98	4 x ☐ = 40
24	4 x ☐ = 40	49	6 x ☐ = 6	74	☐ x 9 = 18	99	☐ x 9 = 9
25	☐ x 9 = 9	50	☐ x 6 = 12	75	5 x ☐ = 5	100	☐ x 5 = 0

Time?	Time?	Time?	Time?
Did you use strategies?	Where can you improve?	Are you improving?	Did you do well?

Exercise 37A	Exercise 37B	Exercise 37C	Exercise 37D
Name:	Name:	Name:	Name:
Date:	Date:	Date:	Date:

1 $\square \times 7 = 35$	**26** $\square \times 8 = 40$	**51** $\square \times 4 = 4$	**76** $2 \times \square = 6$
2 $2 \times \square = 0$	**27** $2 \times \square = 6$	**52** $8 \times \square = 40$	**77** $\square \times 8 = 40$
3 $4 \times \square = 40$	**28** $\square \times 8 = 80$	**53** $\square \times 1 = 3$	**78** $6 \times \square = 0$
4 $\square \times 2 = 8$	**29** $\square \times 4 = 4$	**54** $2 \times \square = 16$	**79** $\square \times 8 = 0$
5 $3 \times \square = 15$	**30** $4 \times \square = 20$	**55** $\square \times 10 = 40$	**80** $\square \times 2 = 8$
6 $\square \times 6 = 6$	**31** $\square \times 2 = 12$	**56** $5 \times \square = 20$	**81** $5 \times \square = 25$
7 $10 \times \square = 40$	**32** $1 \times \square = 5$	**57** $\square \times 4 = 0$	**82** $\square \times 10 = 20$
8 $3 \times \square = 0$	**33** $\square \times 9 = 0$	**58** $2 \times \square = 18$	**83** $6 \times \square = 0$
9 $\square \times 8 = 40$	**34** $\square \times 3 = 15$	**59** $\square \times 1 = 1$	**84** $\square \times 1 = 10$
10 $2 \times \square = 12$	**35** $4 \times \square = 40$	**60** $5 \times \square = 25$	**85** $5 \times \square = 30$
11 $\square \times 6 = 6$	**36** $\square \times 6 = 12$	**61** $\square \times 7 = 70$	**86** $2 \times \square = 18$
12 $4 \times \square = 20$	**37** $7 \times \square = 70$	**62** $\square \times 5 = 45$	**87** $\square \times 5 = 45$
13 $\square \times 10 = 80$	**38** $\square \times 2 = 16$	**63** $4 \times \square = 8$	**88** $\square \times 1 = 6$
14 $9 \times \square = 45$	**39** $5 \times \square = 0$	**64** $\square \times 10 = 30$	**89** $10 \times \square = 70$
15 $3 \times \square = 0$	**40** $\square \times 6 = 30$	**65** $6 \times \square = 30$	**90** $\square \times 5 = 35$
16 $\square \times 5 = 25$	**41** $\square \times 9 = 9$	**66** $\square \times 6 = 0$	**91** $2 \times \square = 18$
17 $2 \times \square = 4$	**42** $4 \times \square = 40$	**67** $1 \times \square = 7$	**92** $\square \times 4 = 0$
18 $\square \times 10 = 70$	**43** $\square \times 2 = 4$	**68** $2 \times \square = 10$	**93** $5 \times \square = 20$
19 $1 \times \square = 4$	**44** $7 \times \square = 35$	**69** $\square \times 3 = 15$	**94** $\square \times 10 = 40$
20 $7 \times \square = 35$	**45** $\square \times 8 = 8$	**70** $2 \times \square = 2$	**95** $2 \times \square = 16$
21 $\square \times 7 = 70$	**46** $10 \times \square = 60$	**71** $\square \times 10 = 0$	**96** $\square \times 1 = 3$
22 $6 \times \square = 6$	**47** $\square \times 2 = 14$	**72** $7 \times \square = 35$	**97** $8 \times \square = 40$
23 $\square \times 5 = 45$	**48** $5 \times \square = 15$	**73** $\square \times 10 = 80$	**98** $\square \times 4 = 4$
24 $2 \times \square = 18$	**49** $\square \times 2 = 10$	**74** $9 \times \square = 18$	**99** $10 \times \square = 60$
25 $\square \times 6 = 30$	**50** $\square \times 6 = 60$	**75** $\square \times 8 = 8$	**100** $5 \times \square = 10$

Time?	Time?	Time?	Time?

How did you do?   Did you beat your best score?   Can you try to be faster?   Have you reached your target?

Exercise 38A	Exercise 38B	Exercise 38C	Exercise 38D
Name:	Name:	Name:	Name:
Date:	Date:	Date:	Date:

#	38A	#	38B	#	38C	#	38D
1	7 x ☐ = 49	26	1 x ☐ = 8	51	2 x ☐ = 4	76	4 x ☐ = 40
2	☐ x 6 = 60	27	☐ x 4 = 16	52	☐ x 5 = 10	77	☐ x 2 = 4
3	5 x ☐ = 10	28	5 x ☐ = 20	53	☐ x 6 = 60	78	☐ x 3 = 15
4	2 x ☐ = 4	29	☐ x 3 = 6	54	7 x ☐ = 49	79	9 x ☐ = 0
5	☐ x 5 = 15	30	1 x ☐ = 1	55	☐ x 4 = 4	80	☐ x 4 = 16
6	7 x ☐ = 14	31	☐ x 5 = 50	56	8 x ☐ = 40	81	1 x ☐ = 5
7	☐ x 8 = 64	32	8 x ☐ = 40	57	6 x ☐ = 36	82	☐ x 7 = 49
8	10 x ☐ = 60	33	☐ x 9 = 81	58	☐ x 1 = 3	83	6 x ☐ = 12
9	☐ x 8 = 8	34	8 x ☐ = 16	59	2 x ☐ = 16	84	4 x ☐ = 20
10	9 x ☐ = 81	35	5 x ☐ = 0	60	☐ x 10 = 40	85	☐ x 3 = 9
11	☐ x 5 = 35	36	☐ x 3 = 9	61	5 x ☐ = 25	86	☐ x 4 = 4
12	2 x ☐ = 4	37	5 x ☐ = 30	62	☐ x 4 = 20	87	10 x ☐ = 80
13	3 x ☐ = 9	38	☐ x 9 = 9	63	1 x ☐ = 1	88	☐ x 9 = 81
14	☐ x 10 = 40	39	8 x ☐ = 64	64	☐ x 4 = 0	89	8 x ☐ = 64
15	4 x ☐ = 16	40	☐ x 4 = 16	65	10 x ☐ = 100	90	☐ x 3 = 6
16	☐ x 3 = 15	41	4 x ☐ = 40	66	☐ x 9 = 18	91	5 x ☐ = 40
17	2 x ☐ = 2	42	☐ x 10 = 100	67	1 x ☐ = 7	92	☐ x 1 = 6
18	☐ x 6 = 36	43	☐ x 3 = 9	68	☐ x 5 = 25	93	9 x ☐ = 81
19	10 x ☐ = 0	44	2 x ☐ = 4	69	10 x ☐ = 70	94	☐ x 8 = 0
20	2 x ☐ = 4	45	7 x ☐ = 35	70	☐ x 5 = 45	95	4 x ☐ = 8
21	☐ x 5 = 35	46	☐ x 9 = 81	71	6 x ☐ = 36	96	☐ x 10 = 100
22	8 x ☐ = 80	47	10 x ☐ = 60	72	☐ x 10 = 70	97	☐ x 5 = 25
23	☐ x 5 = 25	48	☐ x 8 = 64	73	8 x ☐ = 64	98	2 x ☐ = 20
24	9 x ☐ = 18	49	7 x ☐ = 14	74	☐ x 1 = 1	99	☐ x 6 = 36
25	☐ x 10 = 100	50	☐ x 5 = 15	75	☐ x 6 = 12	100	☐ x 9 = 18

Time?	Time?	Time?	Time?
How do you think you are doing?	How did you do?	Is this your best score?	Which facts do you find the easiest?

Exercise 39A

Name:
Date:

1. $8 \times \square = 72$
2. $\square \times 10 = 80$
3. $5 \times \square = 25$
4. $9 \times \square = 18$
5. $\square \times 10 = 100$
6. $3 \times \square = 27$
7. $1 \times \square = 8$
8. $\square \times 4 = 16$
9. $5 \times \square = 20$
10. $4 \times \square = 36$
11. $\square \times 5 = 15$
12. $7 \times \square = 14$
13. $\square \times 8 = 64$
14. $10 \times \square = 60$
15. $\square \times 9 = 27$
16. $1 \times \square = 8$
17. $\square \times 9 = 81$
18. $7 \times \square = 35$
19. $\square \times 2 = 4$
20. $7 \times \square = 63$
21. $\square \times 3 = 9$
22. $10 \times \square = 100$
23. $\square \times 10 = 40$
24. $5 \times \square = 20$
25. $\square \times 9 = 72$

Time?

Did you do well?

Exercise 39B

Name:
Date:

26. $1 \times \square = 1$
27. $\square \times 9 = 54$
28. $2 \times \square = 6$
29. $\square \times 4 = 20$
30. $4 \times \square = 16$
31. $\square \times 8 = 8$
32. $\square \times 9 = 27$
33. $10 \times \square = 100$
34. $\square \times 2 = 18$
35. $\square \times 5 = 25$
36. $8 \times \square = 80$
37. $\square \times 9 = 72$
38. $7 \times \square = 35$
39. $\square \times 2 = 4$
40. $10 \times \square = 0$
41. $\square \times 7 = 49$
42. $4 \times \square = 36$
43. $\square \times 6 = 36$
44. $2 \times \square = 2$
45. $\square \times 3 = 15$
46. $9 \times \square = 81$
47. $\square \times 8 = 80$
48. $1 \times \square = 4$
49. $\square \times 3 = 9$
50. $\square \times 5 = 20$

Time?

What have you learnt today?

Exercise 39C

Name:
Date:

51. $9 \times \square = 54$
52. $\square \times 2 = 12$
53. $\square \times 5 = 40$
54. $6 \times \square = 36$
55. $\square \times 1 = 3$
56. $2 \times \square = 16$
57. $\square \times 10 = 40$
58. $4 \times \square = 36$
59. $\square \times 5 = 25$
60. $1 \times \square = 1$
61. $\square \times 4 = 0$
62. $\square \times 10 = 100$
63. $2 \times \square = 18$
64. $\square \times 7 = 7$
65. $\square \times 9 = 54$
66. $5 \times \square = 25$
67. $10 \times \square = 70$
68. $\square \times 5 = 45$
69. $6 \times \square = 36$
70. $\square \times 10 = 70$
71. $9 \times \square = 63$
72. $\square \times 9 = 36$
73. $\square \times 6 = 36$
74. $2 \times \square = 2$
75. $\square \times 3 = 15$

Time?

Have you reached your target?

Exercise 39D

Name:
Date:

76. $9 \times \square = 81$
77. $\square \times 9 = 72$
78. $10 \times \square = 80$
79. $\square \times 4 = 4$
80. $3 \times \square = 9$
81. $\square \times 5 = 20$
82. $6 \times \square = 54$
83. $2 \times \square = 12$
84. $\square \times 7 = 49$
85. $1 \times \square = 5$
86. $\square \times 4 = 16$
87. $\square \times 5 = 15$
88. $9 \times \square = 0$
89. $\square \times 5 = 25$
90. $3 \times \square = 27$
91. $\square \times 2 = 4$
92. $4 \times \square = 40$
93. $\square \times 6 = 12$
94. $1 \times \square = 1$
95. $\square \times 8 = 64$
96. $7 \times \square = 63$
97. $\square \times 6 = 60$
98. $1 \times \square = 8$
99. $\square \times 9 = 81$
100. $7 \times \square = 35$

Time?

What is your time?

Exercise 40A	Exercise 40B	Exercise 40C	Exercise 40D
Name:	Name:	Name:	Name:
Date:	Date:	Date:	Date:

Exercise 40A

1. ☐ x 1 = 1
2. 2 x ☐ = 12
3. 4 x ☐ = 40
4. ☐ x 2 = 4
5. 3 x ☐ = 27
6. 5 x ☐ = 25
7. ☐ x 9 = 0
8. 5 x ☐ = 15
9. ☐ x 4 = 16
10. 1 x ☐ = 5
11. 3 x ☐ = 15
12. ☐ x 7 = 49
13. 6 x ☐ = 12
14. ☐ x 9 = 54
15. 3 x ☐ = 12
16. 4 x ☐ = 20
17. ☐ x 6 = 18
18. 10 x ☐ = 70
19. ☐ x 5 = 45
20. 6 x ☐ = 36
21. ☐ x 7 = 21
22. 7 x ☐ = 70
23. ☐ x 9 = 63
24. 8 x ☐ = 64
25. 3 x ☐ = 24

Exercise 40B

26. 9 x ☐ = 18
27. ☐ x 6 = 18
28. 5 x ☐ = 25
29. ☐ x 10 = 80
30. 3 x ☐ = 9
31. ☐ x 9 = 72
32. 7 x ☐ = 35
33. ☐ x 2 = 4
34. 3 x ☐ = 12
35. ☐ x 10 = 0
36. 7 x ☐ = 49
37. 4 x ☐ = 36
38. ☐ x 6 = 36
39. 3 x ☐ = 21
40. ☐ x 1 = 2
41. 5 x ☐ = 15
42. 9 x ☐ = 81
43. ☐ x 8 = 24
44. 8 x ☐ = 72
45. ☐ x 8 = 80
46. 1 x ☐ = 4
47. ☐ x 9 = 27
48. 6 x ☐ = 54
49. ☐ x 1 = 1
50. ☐ x 5 = 50

Exercise 40C

51. 8 x ☐ = 40
52. ☐ x 9 = 81
53. 3 x ☐ = 9
54. ☐ x 9 = 63
55. ☐ x 2 = 16
56. 3 x ☐ = 21
57. ☐ x 0 = 0
58. 3 x ☐ = 9
59. ☐ x 6 = 30
60. 8 x ☐ = 40
61. ☐ x 5 = 15
62. 6 x ☐ = 54
63. 1 x ☐ = 4
64. ☐ x 7 = 49
65. 3 x ☐ = 27
66. ☐ x 6 = 36
67. 3 x ☐ = 3
68. ☐ x 4 = 12
69. 2 x ☐ = 16
70. 3 x ☐ = 27
71. 4 x ☐ = 40
72. ☐ x 6 = 18
73. 4 x ☐ = 36
74. ☐ x 5 = 25
75. 3 x ☐ = 24

Exercise 40D

76. 7 x ☐ = 70
77. ☐ x 8 = 64
78. 1 x ☐ = 1
79. 2 x ☐ = 12
80. ☐ x 10 = 40
81. 2 x ☐ = 4
82. ☐ x 9 = 27
83. 5 x ☐ = 25
84. ☐ x 9 = 0
85. 3 x ☐ = 15
86. ☐ x 4 = 16
87. 1 x ☐ = 5
88. 3 x ☐ = 15
89. ☐ x 7 = 21
90. 6 x ☐ = 12
91. ☐ x 9 = 54
92. 2 x ☐ = 4
93. ☐ x 4 = 16
94. 10 x ☐ = 0
95. ☐ x 7 = 49
96. 4 x ☐ = 36
97. 6 x ☐ = 36
98. ☐ x 7 = 21
99. 2 x ☐ = 2
100. ☐ x 3 = 15

Time?	Time?	Time?	Time?

Try to be even quicker next time?

How are you doing?

Try to be faster?

Did you beat your target?

Exercise 41A

Name:

Date:

1. $10 \times \boxed{} = 0$
2. $\boxed{} \times 9 = 63$
3. $2 \times \boxed{} = 4$
4. $4 \times \boxed{} = 12$
5. $\boxed{} \times 5 = 35$
6. $8 \times \boxed{} = 72$
7. $\boxed{} \times 3 = 9$
8. $4 \times \boxed{} = 24$
9. $\boxed{} \times 10 = 80$
10. $5 \times \boxed{} = 25$
11. $3 \times \boxed{} = 18$
12. $\boxed{} \times 9 = 36$
13. $3 \times \boxed{} = 15$
14. $\boxed{} \times 5 = 40$
15. $6 \times \boxed{} = 54$
16. $\boxed{} \times 3 = 9$
17. $5 \times \boxed{} = 0$
18. $\boxed{} \times 7 = 21$
19. $8 \times \boxed{} = 16$
20. $7 \times \boxed{} = 63$
21. $\boxed{} \times 7 = 28$
22. $3 \times \boxed{} = 9$
23. $\boxed{} \times 9 = 81$
24. $8 \times \boxed{} = 40$
25. $\boxed{} \times 8 = 32$

Time?

How did you do?

Exercise 41B

Name:

Date:

26. $3 \times \boxed{} = 18$
27. $\boxed{} \times 5 = 50$
28. $1 \times \boxed{} = 1$
29. $\boxed{} \times 6 = 24$
30. $\boxed{} \times 9 = 54$
31. $2 \times \boxed{} = 6$
32. $\boxed{} \times 4 = 20$
33. $4 \times \boxed{} = 36$
34. $\boxed{} \times 8 = 24$
35. $4 \times \boxed{} = 16$
36. $\boxed{} \times 3 = 15$
37. $\boxed{} \times 8 = 32$
38. $2 \times \boxed{} = 2$
39. $\boxed{} \times 7 = 21$
40. $6 \times \boxed{} = 36$
41. $\boxed{} \times 7 = 28$
42. $7 \times \boxed{} = 49$
43. $\boxed{} \times 10 = 0$
44. $7 \times \boxed{} = 63$
45. $\boxed{} \times 2 = 4$
46. $\boxed{} \times 3 = 12$
47. $8 \times \boxed{} = 72$
48. $\boxed{} \times 10 = 80$
49. $9 \times \boxed{} = 18$
50. $\boxed{} \times 8 = 8$

Time?

Have you reached your target?

Exercise 41C

Name:

Date:

51. $\boxed{} \times 9 = 81$
52. $3 \times \boxed{} = 24$
53. $\boxed{} \times 9 = 36$
54. $10 \times \boxed{} = 80$
55. $\boxed{} \times 4 = 4$
56. $\boxed{} \times 9 = 27$
57. $4 \times \boxed{} = 24$
58. $\boxed{} \times 5 = 20$
59. $3 \times \boxed{} = 12$
60. $\boxed{} \times 9 = 54$
61. $4 \times \boxed{} = 28$
62. $\boxed{} \times 2 = 12$
63. $7 \times \boxed{} = 49$
64. $\boxed{} \times 8 = 32$
65. $3 \times \boxed{} = 15$
66. $\boxed{} \times 5 = 5$
67. $4 \times \boxed{} = 16$
68. $\boxed{} \times 3 = 12$
69. $3 \times \boxed{} = 15$
70. $\boxed{} \times 9 = 0$
71. $5 \times \boxed{} = 25$
72. $\boxed{} \times 9 = 27$
73. $2 \times \boxed{} = 4$
74. $\boxed{} \times 10 = 40$
75. $\boxed{} \times 2 = 16$

Time?

Try to be faster?

Exercise 41D

Name:

Date:

76. $\boxed{} \times 7 = 70$
77. $3 \times \boxed{} = 21$
78. $\boxed{} \times 6 = 36$
79. $\boxed{} \times 5 = 45$
80. $4 \times \boxed{} = 32$
81. $\boxed{} \times 7 = 70$
82. $3 \times \boxed{} = 18$
83. $\boxed{} \times 5 = 25$
84. $4 \times \boxed{} = 36$
85. $\boxed{} \times 5 = 15$
86. $8 \times \boxed{} = 72$
87. $10 \times \boxed{} = 60$
88. $\boxed{} \times 7 = 28$
89. $7 \times \boxed{} = 49$
90. $\boxed{} \times 9 = 27$
91. $\boxed{} \times 6 = 24$
92. $3 \times \boxed{} = 9$
93. $\boxed{} \times 4 = 4$
94. $2 \times \boxed{} = 12$
95. $\boxed{} \times 1 = 1$
96. $3 \times \boxed{} = 24$
97. $\boxed{} \times 8 = 64$
98. $7 \times \boxed{} = 63$
99. $\boxed{} \times 3 = 12$
100. $\boxed{} \times 10 = 70$

Time?

What is your time?

Exercise 42

Missing Box x1, x0, x10, x2, x5, Squares, x9, x3, x4, x6

Exercise 42A	Exercise 42B	Exercise 42C	Exercise 42D
Name:	Name:	Name:	Name:
Date:	Date:	Date:	Date:

Exercise 42A

1. ☐ x 6 = 18
2. 6 x ☐ = 48
3. ☐ x 1 = 1
4. 4 x ☐ = 24
5. ☐ x 8 = 0
6. ☐ x 7 = 7
7. ☐ x 4 = 20
8. 3 x ☐ = 24
9. ☐ x 9 = 54
10. 4 x ☐ = 16
11. ☐ x 8 = 8
12. 3 x ☐ = 18
13. 3 x ☐ = 12
14. ☐ x 5 = 0
15. 4 x ☐ = 28
16. ☐ x 7 = 21
17. 8 x ☐ = 16
18. ☐ x 9 = 63
19. 4 x ☐ = 28
20. ☐ x 3 = 9
21. 9 x ☐ = 81
22. 4 x ☐ = 24
23. ☐ x 4 = 12
24. 6 x ☐ = 54
25. ☐ x 7 = 28

Exercise 42B

26. 6 x ☐ = 42
27. ☐ x 6 = 12
28. 7 x ☐ = 49
29. ☐ x 8 = 32
30. 3 x ☐ = 9
31. ☐ x 1 = 1
32. 6 x ☐ = 42
33. ☐ x 8 = 8
34. 3 x ☐ = 12
35. 6 x ☐ = 54
36. ☐ x 5 = 15
37. 8 x ☐ = 40
38. ☐ x 6 = 30
39. 6 x ☐ = 48
40. ☐ x 3 = 9
41. 4 x ☐ = 12
42. ☐ x 4 = 20
43. 4 x ☐ = 36
44. ☐ x 8 = 24
45. 3 x ☐ = 15
46. ☐ x 9 = 0
47. 6 x ☐ = 54
48. ☐ x 5 = 25
49. 3 x ☐ = 27
50. ☐ x 2 = 4

Exercise 42C

51. 4 x ☐ = 24
52. ☐ x 1 = 1
53. 6 x ☐ = 48
54. ☐ x 6 = 18
55. ☐ x 8 = 32
56. 8 x ☐ = 40
57. ☐ x 9 = 81
58. 6 x ☐ = 42
59. ☐ x 3 = 9
60. 4 x ☐ = 28
61. ☐ x 9 = 63
62. 8 x ☐ = 16
63. ☐ x 3 = 21
64. 4 x ☐ = 28
65. ☐ x 5 = 0
66. 7 x ☐ = 49
67. 4 x ☐ = 32
68. ☐ x 5 = 15
69. ☐ x 5 = 5
70. 4 x ☐ = 16
71. 3 x ☐ = 12
72. ☐ x 9 = 36
73. ☐ x 5 = 15
74. 9 x ☐ = 0
75. ☐ x 9 = 54

Exercise 42D

76. 1 x ☐ = 8
77. ☐ x 4 = 16
78. ☐ x 8 = 24
79. 4 x ☐ = 36
80. ☐ x 4 = 20
81. 4 x ☐ = 28
82. ☐ x 2 = 12
83. 7 x ☐ = 49
84. ☐ x 8 = 32
85. 3 x ☐ = 15
86. 4 x ☐ = 16
87. ☐ x 4 = 12
88. 4 x ☐ = 36
89. ☐ x 5 = 15
90. 9 x ☐ = 0
91. ☐ x 9 = 54
92. 5 x ☐ = 25
93. ☐ x 9 = 27
94. 2 x ☐ = 4
95. ☐ x 10 = 40
96. 2 x ☐ = 2
97. ☐ x 8 = 48
98. 3 x ☐ = 24
99. 7 x ☐ = 63
100. ☐ x 8 = 64

Time? Did you beat your score?

Time? Is this your best score yet?

Time? Try to be even quicker next time!

Time? Did you use any strategies?

Exercise 43A	Exercise 43B	Exercise 43C	Exercise 43D
Name:	Name:	Name:	Name:
Date:	Date:	Date:	Date:

1 ☐ x 6 = 24   **26** ☐ x 10 = 50   **51** ☐ x 4 = 12   **76** 6 x ☐ = 42

2 8 x ☐ = 80   **27** 1 x ☐ = 1   **52** 4 x ☐ = 16   **77** ☐ x 5 = 20

3 ☐ x 8 = 56   **28** ☐ x 6 = 24   **53** ☐ x 5 = 15   **78** 3 x ☐ = 24

4 5 x ☐ = 25   **29** ☐ x 7 = 49   **54** 3 x ☐ = 12   **79** ☐ x 9 = 54

5 1 x ☐ = 8   **30** 6 x ☐ = 54   **55** ☐ x 7 = 42   **80** 3 x ☐ = 15

6 ☐ x 6 = 18   **31** ☐ x 8 = 48   **56** 8 x ☐ = 40   **81** 3 x ☐ = 27

7 6 x ☐ = 42   **32** 2 x ☐ = 6   **57** ☐ x 6 = 18   **82** ☐ x 10 = 100

8 ☐ x 9 = 18   **33** ☐ x 7 = 28   **58** 10 x ☐ = 50   **83** 9 x ☐ = 18

9 10 x ☐ = 100   **34** 4 x ☐ = 20   **59** ☐ x 7 = 63   **84** ☐ x 7 = 42

10 ☐ x 9 = 27   **35** ☐ x 9 = 36   **60** 1 x ☐ = 1   **85** 3 x ☐ = 18

11 3 x ☐ = 15   **36** ☐ x 8 = 24   **61** ☐ x 6 = 24   **86** ☐ x 8 = 8

12 4 x ☐ = 12   **37** 3 x ☐ = 18   **62** 5 x ☐ = 40   **87** 5 x ☐ = 25

13 ☐ x 7 = 42   **38** ☐ x 8 = 8   **63** ☐ x 6 = 18   **88** 7 x ☐ = 56

14 1 x ☐ = 8   **39** 5 x ☐ = 25   **64** 2 x ☐ = 4   **89** ☐ x 10 = 80

15 ☐ x 4 = 16   **40** ☐ x 8 = 56   **65** 4 x ☐ = 40   **90** ☐ x 6 = 24

16 8 x ☐ = 40   **41** ☐ x 10 = 80   **66** ☐ x 1 = 2   **91** 6 x ☐ = 54

17 ☐ x 6 = 18   **42** 4 x ☐ = 24   **67** 3 x ☐ = 21   **92** ☐ x 9 = 63

18 5 x ☐ = 50   **43** ☐ x 9 = 54   **68** ☐ x 8 = 48   **93** 4 x ☐ = 24

19 7 x ☐ = 63   **44** 7 x ☐ = 63   **69** 3 x ☐ = 18   **94** ☐ x 4 = 12

20 ☐ x 1 = 1   **45** ☐ x 6 = 24   **70** 6 x ☐ = 36   **95** 6 x ☐ = 54

21 4 x ☐ = 24   **46** ☐ x 4 = 12   **71** ☐ x 8 = 56   **96** ☐ x 7 = 28

22 ☐ x 8 = 40   **47** ☐ x 9 = 54   **72** 1 x ☐ = 1   **97** 4 x ☐ = 40

23 3 x ☐ = 18   **48** 4 x ☐ = 28   **73** ☐ x 6 = 24   **98** ☐ x 2 = 4

24 ☐ x 6 = 0   **49** ☐ x 7 = 35   **74** 8 x ☐ = 0   **99** 3 x ☐ = 27

25 ☐ x 8 = 40   **50** 6 x ☐ = 42   **75** ☐ x 7 = 7   **100** 5 x ☐ = 25

Time?   Time?   Time?   Time?

Which facts did you find the hardest?   Did you beat your target?   Can you try to be faster?   Where do you need to improve?

Exercise 44A

Name:
Date:

1. $7 \times \square = 56$
2. $\square \times 4 = 20$
3. $4 \times \square = 28$
4. $8 \times \square = 64$
5. $\square \times 3 = 6$
6. $6 \times \square = 54$
7. $\square \times 7 = 49$
8. $5 \times \square = 40$
9. $\square \times 6 = 24$
10. $1 \times \square = 1$
11. $\square \times 9 = 72$
12. $5 \times \square = 50$
13. $\square \times 8 = 32$
14. $\square \times 6 = 0$
15. $7 \times \square = 56$
16. $\square \times 6 = 18$
17. $3 \times \square = 24$
18. $\square \times 6 = 24$
19. $1 \times \square = 1$
20. $7 \times \square = 63$
21. $\square \times 6 = 48$
22. $5 \times \square = 50$
23. $\square \times 6 = 18$
24. $4 \times \square = 40$
25. $4 \times \square = 32$

Exercise 44B

Name:
Date:

26. $4 \times \square = 32$
27. $\square \times 9 = 54$
28. $4 \times \square = 24$
29. $8 \times \square = 80$
30. $\square \times 8 = 56$
31. $5 \times \square = 25$
32. $\square \times 8 = 8$
33. $3 \times \square = 18$
34. $\square \times 7 = 56$
35. $3 \times \square = 18$
36. $6 \times \square = 42$
37. $\square \times 8 = 64$
38. $2 \times \square = 18$
39. $\square \times 10 = 100$
40. $5 \times \square = 40$
41. $\square \times 9 = 27$
42. $3 \times \square = 15$
43. $3 \times \square = 12$
44. $\square \times 9 = 72$
45. $6 \times \square = 42$
46. $\square \times 3 = 24$
47. $3 \times \square = 12$
48. $1 \times \square = 8$
49. $\square \times 6 = 48$
50. $4 \times \square = 16$

Exercise 44C

Name:
Date:

51. $4 \times \square = 36$
52. $\square \times 5 = 20$
53. $4 \times \square = 32$
54. $\square \times 7 = 28$
55. $\square \times 3 = 6$
56. $6 \times \square = 48$
57. $\square \times 7 = 56$
58. $7 \times \square = 49$
59. $\square \times 6 = 24$
60. $5 \times \square = 40$
61. $\square \times 10 = 50$
62. $\square \times 8 = 32$
63. $6 \times \square = 0$
64. $\square \times 7 = 56$
65. $3 \times \square = 18$
66. $\square \times 6 = 48$
67. $1 \times \square = 1$
68. $7 \times \square = 63$
69. $\square \times 8 = 64$
70. $7 \times \square = 63$
71. $\square \times 6 = 18$
72. $5 \ \square = 40$
73. $\square \times 9 = 81$
74. $3 \times \square = 9$
75. $\square \times 9 = 72$

Exercise 44D

Name:
Date:

76. $8 \times \square = 64$
77. $\square \times 7 = 42$
78. $3 \times \square = 24$
79. $\square \times 5 = 20$
80. $1 \times \square = 7$
81. $4 \times \square = 32$
82. $\square \times 8 = 0$
83. $4 \times \square = 24$
84. $\square \times 1 = 1$
85. $6 \times \square = 48$
86. $\square \times 8 = 40$
87. $3 \times \square = 24$
88. $\square \times 7 = 28$
89. $9 \times \square = 81$
90. $7 \times \square = 56$
91. $\square \times 9 = 54$
92. $1 \times \square = 1$
93. $\square \times 4 = 32$
94. $5 \times \square = 50$
95. $\square \times 6 = 18$
96. $8 \times \square = 48$
97. $\square \times 10 = 50$
98. $4 \times \square = 32$
99. $\square \times 9 = 72$
100. $\square \times 3 = 9$

Time? — Is this your best score?

Time? — Have you reached your target?

Time? — Did you do well?

Time? — Do you think you are improving?

Exercise 45A	Exercise 45B	Exercise 45C	Exercise 45D
Name:	Name:	Name:	Name:
Date:	Date:	Date:	Date:

#	45A	#	45B	#	45C	#	45D
1	$70 \div 10 =$	26	$40 \div 10 =$	51	$6 \div 1 =$	76	$2 \div 1 =$
2	$4 \div 1 =$	27	$1 \div 1 =$	52	$100 \div 10 =$	77	$40 \div 10 =$
3	$3 \div 1 =$	28	$80 \div 10 =$	53	$9 \div 1 =$	78	$7 \div 1 =$
4	$30 \div 10 =$	29	$7 \div 1 =$	54	$70 \div 10 =$	79	$3 \div 1 =$
5	$8 \div 1 =$	30	$90 \div 10 =$	55	$1 \div 1 =$	80	$60 \div 10 =$
6	$20 \div 10 =$	31	$9 \div 1 =$	56	$4 \div 1 =$	81	$5 \div 1 =$
7	$7 \div 1 =$	32	$2 \div 1 =$	57	$20 \div 10 =$	82	$50 \div 10 =$
8	$3 \div 1 =$	33	$100 \div 10 =$	58	$40 \div 10 =$	83	$8 \div 1 =$
9	$50 \div 10 =$	34	$6 \div 1 =$	59	$7 \div 1 =$	84	$60 \div 10 =$
10	$6 \div 1 =$	35	$8 \div 1 =$	60	$10 \div 1 =$	85	$4 \div 1 =$
11	$4 \div 1 =$	36	$50 \div 10 =$	61	$80 \div 10 =$	86	$100 \div 10 =$
12	$40 \div 10 =$	37	$5 \div 1 =$	62	$30 \div 10 =$	87	$80 \div 10 =$
13	$6 \div 1 =$	38	$10 \div 10 =$	63	$2 \div 1 =$	88	$9 \div 1 =$
14	$60 \div 10 =$	39	$3 \div 1 =$	64	$9 \div 1 =$	89	$70 \div 10 =$
15	$10 \div 1 =$	40	$30 \div 10 =$	65	$60 \div 10 =$	90	$6 \div 1 =$
16	$30 \div 10 =$	41	$10 \div 1 =$	66	$3 \div 1 =$	91	$100 \div 10 =$
17	$5 \div 1 =$	42	$2 \div 1 =$	67	$90 \div 10 =$	92	$10 \div 1 =$
18	$70 \div 10 =$	43	$60 \div 10 =$	68	$50 \div 10 =$	93	$7 \div 1 =$
19	$2 \div 1 =$	44	$4 \div 1 =$	69	$4 \div 1 =$	94	$20 \div 10 =$
20	$8 \div 1 =$	45	$20 \div 10 =$	70	$100 \div 10 =$	95	$10 \div 10 =$
21	$10 \div 10 =$	46	$1 \div 1 =$	71	$70 \div 10 =$	96	$30 \div 10 =$
22	$10 \div 1 =$	47	$40 \div 10 =$	72	$5 \div 1 =$	97	$1 \div 1 =$
23	$80 \div 10 =$	48	$5 \div 1 =$	73	$10 \div 10 =$	98	$8 \div 1 =$
24	$4 \div 1 =$	49	$70 \div 10 =$	74	$8 \div 1 =$	99	$40 \div 10 =$
25	$70 \div 10 =$	50	$30 \div 10 =$	75	$40 \div 10 =$	100	$7 \div 1 =$

Time? | Time? | Time? | Time?

Try to concentrate even more! | How do you think you are doing? | What have you learnt today? | How could you recall these facts even quicker?

Exercise 46A	Exercise 46B	Exercise 46C	Exercise 46D
Name:	Name:	Name:	Name:
Date:	Date:	Date:	Date:

Exercise 46A
1. $12 \div 2 =$
2. $6 \div 1 =$
3. $30 \div 10 =$
4. $8 \div 2 =$
5. $9 \div 1 =$
6. $100 \div 10 =$
7. $70 \div 10 =$
8. $3 \div 1 =$
9. $14 \div 2 =$
10. $10 \div 1 =$
11. $30 \div 10 =$
12. $2 \div 2 =$
13. $8 \div 1 =$
14. $40 \div 10 =$
15. $70 \div 10 =$
16. $1 \div 1 =$
17. $2 \div 1 =$
18. $4 \div 2 =$
19. $50 \div 10 =$
20. $9 \div 1 =$
21. $60 \div 10 =$
22. $5 \div 1 =$
23. $6 \div 2 =$
24. $3 \div 1 =$
25. $10 \div 2 =$

Exercise 46B
26. $6 \div 1 =$
27. $14 \div 2 =$
28. $2 \div 1 =$
29. $20 \div 10 =$
30. $7 \div 1 =$
31. $18 \div 2 =$
32. $10 \div 10 =$
33. $4 \div 1 =$
34. $10 \div 2 =$
35. $80 \div 10 =$
36. $9 \div 1 =$
37. $18 \div 2 =$
38. $2 \div 1 =$
39. $20 \div 10 =$
40. $40 \div 10 =$
41. $10 \div 1 =$
42. $2 \div 2 =$
43. $7 \div 1 =$
44. $30 \div 10 =$
45. $2 \div 1 =$
46. $16 \div 2 =$
47. $4 \div 1 =$
48. $60 \div 10 =$
49. $4 \div 2 =$
50. $70 \div 10 =$

Exercise 46C
51. $3 \div 1 =$
52. $6 \div 2 =$
53. $5 \div 1 =$
54. $20 \div 10 =$
55. $14 \div 2 =$
56. $9 \div 1 =$
57. $100 \div 10 =$
58. $8 \div 2 =$
59. $3 \div 1 =$
60. $10 \div 10 =$
61. $16 \div 2 =$
62. $7 \div 1 =$
63. $90 \div 10 =$
64. $8 \div 2 =$
65. $1 \div 1 =$
66. $40 \div 10 =$
67. $5 \div 1 =$
68. $50 \div 10 =$
69. $20 \div 2 =$
70. $6 \div 1 =$
71. $50 \div 10 =$
72. $10 \div 1 =$
73. $2 \div 2 =$
74. $80 \div 10 =$
75. $18 \div 2 =$

Exercise 46D
76. $10 \div 2 =$
77. $4 \div 1 =$
78. $10 \div 10 =$
79. $8 \div 1 =$
80. $6 \div 2 =$
81. $100 \div 10 =$
82. $90 \div 10 =$
83. $6 \div 1 =$
84. $16 \div 2 =$
85. $90 \div 10 =$
86. $1 \div 1 =$
87. $12 \div 2 =$
88. $60 \div 10 =$
89. $8 \div 1 =$
90. $18 \div 2 =$
91. $20 \div 10 =$
92. $80 \div 10 =$
93. $4 \div 1 =$
94. $14 \div 2 =$
95. $70 \div 10 =$
96. $1 \div 1 =$
97. $4 \div 2 =$
98. $70 \div 10 =$
99. $7 \div 1 =$
100. $60 \div 10 =$

Time? Time? Time? Time?

Are the facts at your fingertips? | Try to really focus! | Which facts do you find the easiest? | Did you do well?

Exercise 47A	Exercise 47B	Exercise 47C	Exercise 47D
Name:	Name:	Name:	Name:
Date:	Date:	Date:	Date:

#	47A	#	47B	#	47C	#	47D
1	$90 \div 10 =$	26	$25 \div 5 =$	51	$20 \div 10 =$	76	$20 \div 5 =$
2	$6 \div 1 =$	27	$5 \div 1 =$	52	$35 \div 5 =$	77	$70 \div 10 =$
3	$16 \div 2 =$	28	$50 \div 10 =$	53	$5 \div 1 =$	78	$1 \div 1 =$
4	$25 \div 5 =$	29	$20 \div 2 =$	54	$6 \div 2 =$	79	$50 \div 5 =$
5	$90 \div 10 =$	30	$6 \div 1 =$	55	$3 \div 1 =$	80	$2 \div 1 =$
6	$1 \div 1 =$	31	$5 \div 5 =$	56	$15 \div 5 =$	81	$4 \div 2 =$
7	$50 \div 5 =$	32	$50 \div 10 =$	57	$14 \div 2 =$	82	$45 \div 5 =$
8	$12 \div 2 =$	33	$10 \div 1 =$	58	$2 \div 1 =$	83	$50 \div 10 =$
9	$60 \div 10 =$	34	$35 \div 5 =$	59	$20 \div 10 =$	84	$9 \div 1 =$
10	$8 \div 1 =$	35	$2 \div 2 =$	60	$7 \div 1 =$	85	$5 \div 5 =$
11	$18 \div 2 =$	36	$80 \div 10 =$	61	$45 \div 5 =$	86	$60 \div 10 =$
12	$45 \div 5 =$	37	$10 \div 5 =$	62	$18 \div 2 =$	87	$50 \div 5 =$
13	$80 \div 10 =$	38	$7 \div 1 =$	63	$10 \div 10 =$	88	$4 \div 1 =$
14	$4 \div 1 =$	39	$16 \div 2 =$	64	$5 \div 5 =$	89	$16 \div 2 =$
15	$14 \div 2 =$	40	$10 \div 10 =$	65	$4 \div 1 =$	90	$40 \div 5 =$
16	$70 \div 10 =$	41	$20 \div 5 =$	66	$10 \div 2 =$	91	$2 \div 1 =$
17	$15 \div 5 =$	42	$3 \div 1 =$	67	$80 \div 10 =$	92	$30 \div 10 =$
18	$1 \div 1 =$	43	$10 \div 5 =$	68	$15 \div 5 =$	93	$10 \div 5 =$
19	$4 \div 2 =$	44	$8 \div 2 =$	69	$9 \div 1 =$	94	$7 \div 1 =$
20	$40 \div 5 =$	45	$100 \div 10 =$	70	$18 \div 2 =$	95	$2 \div 2 =$
21	$70 \div 10 =$	46	$20 \div 5 =$	71	$30 \div 5 =$	96	$5 \div 5 =$
22	$7 \div 1 =$	47	$9 \div 1 =$	72	$2 \div 1 =$	97	$10 \div 1 =$
23	$40 \div 10 =$	48	$40 \div 5 =$	73	$20 \div 10 =$	98	$40 \div 10 =$
24	$25 \div 5 =$	49	$14 \div 2 =$	74	$50 \div 5 =$	99	$35 \div 5 =$
25	$18 \div 2 =$	50	$70 \div 10 =$	75	$2 \div 2 =$	100	$10 \div 2 =$

Time?	Time?	Time?	Time?
Did you beat you score?	Which facts do you find the hardest?	Is this your best score?	Try to concentrate even more?

Exercise 48A	Exercise 48B	Exercise 48C	Exercise 48D
Name:	Name:	Name:	Name:
Date:	Date:	Date:	Date:

1 $45 \div 5 =$	**26** $14 \div 2 =$	**51** $20 \div 10 =$	**76** $16 \div 2 =$
2 $50 \div 10 =$	**27** $20 \div 10 =$	**52** $7 \div 1 =$	**77** $100 \div 10 =$
3 $49 \div 7 =$	**28** $6 \div 1 =$	**53** $9 \div 3 =$	**78** $4 \div 1 =$
4 $9 \div 1 =$	**29** $16 \div 4 =$	**54** $45 \div 5 =$	**79** $50 \div 5 =$
5 $5 \div 5 =$	**30** $50 \div 10 =$	**55** $18 \div 2 =$	**80** $25 \div 5 =$
6 $60 \div 10 =$	**31** $10 \div 1 =$	**56** $10 \div 10 =$	**81** $60 \div 10 =$
7 $50 \div 5 =$	**32** $35 \div 5 =$	**57** $5 \div 5 =$	**82** $5 \div 5 =$
8 $64 \div 8 =$	**33** $2 \div 2 =$	**58** $16 \div 4 =$	**83** $9 \div 1 =$
9 $4 \div 1 =$	**34** $64 \div 8 =$	**59** $4 \div 1 =$	**84** $81 \div 9 =$
10 $16 \div 2 =$	**35** $80 \div 10 =$	**60** $10 \div 2 =$	**85** $50 \div 10 =$
11 $40 \div 5 =$	**36** $10 \div 5 =$	**61** $80 \div 10 =$	**86** $45 \div 5 =$
12 $2 \div 1 =$	**37** $7 \div 1 =$	**62** $15 \div 5 =$	**87** $4 \div 2 =$
13 $4 \div 2 =$	**38** $16 \div 2 =$	**63** $100 \div 10 =$	**88** $81 \div 9 =$
14 $30 \div 10 =$	**39** $9 \div 3 =$	**64** $9 \div 1 =$	**89** $2 \div 1 =$
15 $10 \div 5 =$	**40** $10 \div 10 =$	**65** $18 \div 2 =$	**90** $50 \div 5 =$
16 $7 \div 1 =$	**41** $20 \div 5 =$	**66** $30 \div 5 =$	**91** $15 \div 5 =$
17 $2 \div 2 =$	**42** $1 \div 1 =$	**67** $64 \div 8 =$	**92** $14 \div 2 =$
18 $36 \div 6 =$	**43** $40 \div 5 =$	**68** $2 \div 1 =$	**93** $36 \div 6 =$
19 $5 \div 5 =$	**44** $70 \div 10 =$	**69** $20 \div 10 =$	**94** $2 \div 1 =$
20 $10 \div 1 =$	**45** $20 \div 5 =$	**70** $50 \div 5 =$	**95** $20 \div 10 =$
21 $40 \div 10 =$	**46** $9 \div 1 =$	**71** $30 \div 10 =$	**96** $7 \div 1 =$
22 $35 \div 5 =$	**47** $40 \div 5 =$	**72** $2 \div 1 =$	**97** $49 \div 7 =$
23 $20 \div 10 =$	**48** $14 \div 2 =$	**73** $25 \div 5 =$	**98** $45 \div 5 =$
24 $4 \div 2 =$	**49** $49 \div 7 =$	**74** $40 \div 5 =$	**99** $18 \div 2 =$
25 $64 \div 8 =$	**50** $70 \div 10 =$	**75** $81 \div 9 =$	**100** $70 \div 10 =$

Time?	Time?	Time?	Time?
Is this your best score yet?	Did you beat your target?	Have you reached your target yet?	How do you think you are doing?

Exercise 49A	Exercise 49B	Exercise 49C	Exercise 49D
Name:	Name:	Name:	Name:
Date:	Date:	Date:	Date:

1 $54 \div 9 =$	**26** $20 \div 10 =$	**51** $81 \div 9 =$	**76** $90 \div 9 =$
2 $50 \div 10 =$	**27** $9 \div 9 =$	**52** $14 \div 2 =$	**77** $50 \div 5 =$
3 $45 \div 5 =$	**28** $6 \div 1 =$	**53** $20 \div 10 =$	**78** $30 \div 10 =$
4 $4 \div 2 =$	**29** $16 \div 4 =$	**54** $7 \div 1 =$	**79** $2 \div 1 =$
5 $81 \div 9 =$	**30** $50 \div 10 =$	**55** $9 \div 3 =$	**80** $72 \div 9 =$
6 $36 \div 9 =$	**31** $27 \div 9 =$	**56** $45 \div 9 =$	**81** $25 \div 5 =$
7 $2 \div 1 =$	**32** $10 \div 1 =$	**57** $18 \div 2 =$	**82** $40 \div 5 =$
8 $50 \div 5 =$	**33** $35 \div 5 =$	**58** $10 \div 10 =$	**83** $16 \div 2 =$
9 $15 \div 5 =$	**34** $2 \div 2 =$	**59** $5 \div 5 =$	**84** $63 \div 9 =$
10 $72 \div 9 =$	**35** $54 \div 9 =$	**60** $16 \div 4 =$	**85** $100 \div 10 =$
11 $14 \div 2 =$	**36** $64 \div 8 =$	**61** $18 \div 9 =$	**86** $4 \div 1 =$
12 $36 \div 6 =$	**37** $80 \div 10 =$	**62** $4 \div 1 =$	**87** $50 \div 5 =$
13 $45 \div 9 =$	**38** $10 \div 5 =$	**63** $10 \div 2 =$	**88** $27 \div 9 =$
14 $2 \div 1 =$	**39** $7 \div 1 =$	**64** $80 \div 10 =$	**89** $25 \div 5 =$
15 $20 \div 10 =$	**40** $16 \div 2 =$	**65** $15 \div 5 =$	**90** $60 \div 10 =$
16 $45 \div 9 =$	**41** $81 \div 9 =$	**66** $100 \div 10 =$	**91** $5 \div 5 =$
17 $7 \div 1 =$	**42** $9 \div 3 =$	**67** $63 \div 9 =$	**92** $9 \div 1 =$
18 $49 \div 7 =$	**43** $10 \div 10 =$	**68** $9 \div 1 =$	**93** $81 \div 9 =$
19 $40 \div 4 =$	**44** $20 \div 5 =$	**69** $18 \div 2 =$	**94** $50 \div 10 =$
20 $54 \div 9 =$	**45** $1 \div 1 =$	**70** $30 \div 5 =$	**95** $45 \div 5 =$
21 $18 \div 2 =$	**46** $90 \div 9 =$	**71** $36 \div 9 =$	**96** $4 \div 2 =$
22 $14 \div 2 =$	**47** $40 \div 5 =$	**72** $64 \div 8 =$	**97** $15 \div 5 =$
23 $40 \div 5 =$	**48** $70 \div 10 =$	**73** $2 \div 1 =$	**98** $50 \div 5 =$
24 $9 \div 1 =$	**49** $20 \div 5 =$	**74** $20 \div 10 =$	**99** $45 \div 9 =$
25 $63 \div 9 =$	**50** $64 \div 8 =$	**75** $35 \div 5 =$	**100** $49 \div 7 =$

Time?	Time?	Time?	Time?
Try to be even quicker next time!	Can you try to be faster?	Did you do well?	What have you learnt today?

Exercise 50A

Name:
Date:

① 9 ÷ 9 =
② 6 ÷ 1 =
③ 15 ÷ 3 =
④ 16 ÷ 4 =
⑤ 27 ÷ 9 =
⑥ 10 ÷ 1 =
⑦ 27 ÷ 3 =
⑧ 35 ÷ 5 =
⑨ 18 ÷ 9 =
⑩ 64 ÷ 8 =
⑪ 12 ÷ 3 =
⑫ 80 ÷ 10 =
⑬ 81 ÷ 9 =
⑭ 21 ÷ 3 =
⑮ 10 ÷ 5 =
⑯ 36 ÷ 9 =
⑰ 30 ÷ 3 =
⑱ 16 ÷ 2 =
⑲ 45 ÷ 9 =
⑳ 10 ÷ 10 =
㉑ 20 ÷ 5 =
㉒ 18 ÷ 3 =
㉓ 50 ÷ 5 =
㉔ 15 ÷ 5 =
㉕ 27 ÷ 3 =

Time?

Did you use strategies?

Exercise 50B

Name:
Date:

㉖ 81 ÷ 9 =
㉗ 4 ÷ 2 =
㉘ 45 ÷ 5 =
㉙ 6 ÷ 3 =
㉚ 27 ÷ 9 =
㉛ 50 ÷ 10 =
㉜ 90 ÷ 9 =
㉝ 9 ÷ 1 =
㉞ 24 ÷ 3 =
㉟ 5 ÷ 5 =
㊱ 60 ÷ 60 =
㊲ 27 ÷ 3 =
㊳ 90 ÷ 9 =
㊴ 25 ÷ 5 =
㊵ 4 ÷ 1 =
㊶ 9 ÷ 3 =
㊷ 100 ÷ 10 =
㊸ 63 ÷ 9 =
㊹ 3 ÷ 3 =
㊺ 16 ÷ 2 =
㊻ 40 ÷ 5 =
㊼ 72 ÷ 9 =
㊽ 30 ÷ 3 =
㊾ 2 ÷ 1 =
㊿ 70 ÷ 10 =

Time?

Where can you improve?

Exercise 50C

Name:
Date:

(51) 27 ÷ 3 =
(52) 30 ÷ 10 =
(53) 18 ÷ 9 =
(54) 50 ÷ 5 =
(55) 18 ÷ 3 =
(56) 90 ÷ 10 =
(57) 54 ÷ 9 =
(58) 12 ÷ 3 =
(59) 20 ÷ 10 =
(60) 9 ÷ 9 =
(61) 6 ÷ 3 =
(62) 7 ÷ 1 =
(63) 18 ÷ 2 =
(64) 27 ÷ 3 =
(65) 45 ÷ 9 =
(66) 10 ÷ 10 =
(67) 30 ÷ 3 =
(68) 16 ÷ 4 =
(69) 18 ÷ 9 =
(70) 21 ÷ 3 =
(71) 64 ÷ 8 =
(72) 14 ÷ 2 =
(73) 72 ÷ 9 =
(74) 12 ÷ 3 =
(75) 49 ÷ 7 =

Time?

Are you improving?

Exercise 50D

Name:
Date:

(76) 3 ÷ 3 =
(77) 36 ÷ 6 =
(78) 45 ÷ 9 =
(79) 2 ÷ 1 =
(80) 24 ÷ 3 =
(81) 20 ÷ 10 =
(82) 63 ÷ 9 =
(83) 12 ÷ 3 =
(84) 49 ÷ 7 =
(85) 40 ÷ 4 =
(86) 81 ÷ 9 =
(87) 21 ÷ 3 =
(88) 18 ÷ 2 =
(89) 14 ÷ 2 =
(90) 15 ÷ 3 =
(91) 40 ÷ 5 =
(92) 9 ÷ 9 =
(93) 9 ÷ 3 =
(94) 25 ÷ 5 =
(95) 50 ÷ 10 =
(96) 27 ÷ 9 =
(97) 10 ÷ 1 =
(98) 35 ÷ 5 =
(99) 27 ÷ 3 =
(100) 80 ÷ 10 =

Time?

Did you do well?

Exercise 50 Division ÷1, ÷10, ÷2, ÷5, Squares, ÷9, ÷3

Exercise 51A	Exercise 51B	Exercise 51C	Exercise 51D
Name:	Name:	Name:	Name:
Date:	Date:	Date:	Date:

1 $20 \div 10 =$	**26** $24 \div 4 =$	**51** $24 \div 3 =$	**76** $20 \div 4 =$
2 $81 \div 9 =$	**27** $27 \div 3 =$	**52** $9 \div 1 =$	**77** $81 \div 9 =$
3 $24 \div 4 =$	**28** $18 \div 2 =$	**53** $32 \div 4 =$	**78** $21 \div 3 =$
4 $21 \div 3 =$	**29** $7 \div 1 =$	**54** $90 \div 9 =$	**79** $10 \div 5 =$
5 $18 \div 2 =$	**30** $32 \div 4 =$	**55** $50 \div 10 =$	**80** $32 \div 4 =$
6 $14 \div 2 =$	**31** $6 \div 3 =$	**56** $27 \div 9 =$	**81** $36 \div 9 =$
7 $16 \div 4 =$	**32** $20 \div 10 =$	**57** $20 \div 4 =$	**82** $30 \div 3 =$
8 $15 \div 3 =$	**33** $12 \div 3 =$	**58** $6 \div 3 =$	**83** $16 \div 2 =$
9 $40 \div 5 =$	**34** $54 \div 9 =$	**59** $45 \div 5 =$	**84** $45 \div 9 =$
10 $32 \div 4 =$	**35** $90 \div 10 =$	**60** $4 \div 2 =$	**85** $4 \div 4 =$
11 $9 \div 9 =$	**36** $20 \div 4 =$	**61** $9 \div 9 =$	**86** $10 \div 10 =$
12 $9 \div 3 =$	**37** $18 \div 3 =$	**62** $16 \div 4 =$	**87** $20 \div 5 =$
13 $25 \div 5 =$	**38** $50 \div 5 =$	**63** $6 \div 1 =$	**88** $18 \div 3 =$
14 $50 \div 10 =$	**39** $18 \div 9 =$	**64** $15 \div 3 =$	**89** $16 \div 4 =$
15 $36 \div 4 =$	**40** $30 \div 10 =$	**65** $27 \div 9 =$	**90** $50 \div 5 =$
16 $27 \div 9 =$	**41** $36 \div 4 =$	**66** $10 \div 1 =$	**91** $15 \div 3 =$
17 $10 \div 1 =$	**42** $2 \div 1 =$	**67** $24 \div 4 =$	**92** $100 \div 10 =$
18 $35 \div 5 =$	**43** $30 \div 3 =$	**68** $27 \div 3 =$	**93** $63 \div 9 =$
19 $27 \div 3 =$	**44** $72 \div 9 =$	**69** $35 \div 5 =$	**94** $3 \div 3 =$
20 $12 \div 3 =$	**45** $40 \div 5 =$	**70** $18 \div 9 =$	**95** $24 \div 4 =$
21 $20 \div 4 =$	**46** $16 \div 4 =$	**71** $20 \div 4 =$	**96** $16 \div 2 =$
22 $72 \div 9 =$	**47** $4 \div 1 =$	**72** $64 \div 8 =$	**97** $40 \div 5 =$
23 $14 \div 2 =$	**48** $25 \div 5 =$	**73** $12 \div 3 =$	**98** $72 \div 9 =$
24 $64 \div 8 =$	**49** $90 \div 9 =$	**74** $80 \div 10 =$	**99** $2 \div 1 =$
25 $45 \div 5 =$	**50** $64 \div 8 =$	**75** $100 \div 10 =$	**100** $27 \div 3 =$

Time?	Time?	Time?	Time?
How did you do?	Did you beat your best score?	Can you try to be faster?	Have you reached your target?

Exercise 52A	Exercise 52B	Exercise 52C	Exercise 52D
Name:	Name:	Name:	Name:
Date:	Date:	Date:	Date:

1 $36 \div 9 =$	26 $80 \div 10 =$	51 $24 \div 6 =$	76 $48 \div 6 =$
2 $30 \div 3 =$	27 $48 \div 6 =$	52 $50 \div 10 =$	77 $30 \div 10 =$
3 $16 \div 2 =$	28 $12 \div 3 =$	53 $90 \div 9 =$	78 $36 \div 4 =$
4 $24 \div 6 =$	29 $64 \div 8 =$	54 $32 \div 4 =$	79 $24 \div 6 =$
5 $45 \div 9 =$	30 $20 \div 4 =$	55 $42 \div 6 =$	80 $2 \div 1 =$
6 $4 \div 4 =$	31 $18 \div 9 =$	56 $9 \div 1 =$	81 $30 \div 3 =$
7 $100 \div 10 =$	32 $35 \div 5 =$	57 $24 \div 3 =$	82 $42 \div 6 =$
8 $36 \div 6 =$	33 $24 \div 6 =$	58 $27 \div 3 =$	83 $72 \div 9 =$
9 $20 \div 5 =$	34 $27 \div 3 =$	59 $18 \div 2 =$	84 $40 \div 5 =$
10 $18 \div 3 =$	35 $24 \div 4 =$	60 $18 \div 6 =$	85 $16 \div 4 =$
11 $16 \div 4 =$	36 $10 \div 1 =$	61 $7 \div 1 =$	86 $4 \div 1 =$
12 $48 \div 6 =$	37 $18 \div 6 =$	62 $32 \div 4 =$	87 $25 \div 5 =$
13 $50 \div 5 =$	38 $27 \div 9 =$	63 $30 \div 6 =$	88 $36 \div 4 =$
14 $15 \div 3 =$	39 $15 \div 3 =$	64 $6 \div 3 =$	89 $30 \div 6 =$
15 $63 \div 9 =$	40 $6 \div 1 =$	65 $20 \div 10 =$	90 $27 \div 9 =$
16 $18 \div 6 =$	41 $16 \div 4 =$	66 $36 \div 6 =$	91 $10 \div 1 =$
17 $3 \div 3 =$	42 $9 \div 9 =$	67 $12 \div 3 =$	92 $35 \div 5 =$
18 $24 \div 4 =$	43 $4 \div 2 =$	68 $54 \div 9 =$	93 $36 \div 6 =$
19 $16 \div 2 =$	44 $36 \div 6 =$	69 $90 \div 10 =$	94 $27 \div 3 =$
20 $40 \div 5 =$	45 $45 \div 5 =$	70 $20 \div 4 =$	95 $12 \div 3 =$
21 $42 \div 6 =$	46 $6 \div 3 =$	71 $18 \div 3 =$	96 $20 \div 4 =$
22 $72 \div 9 =$	47 $20 \div 4 =$	72 $48 \div 6 =$	97 $72 \div 9 =$
23 $2 \div 1 =$	48 $27 \div 9 =$	73 $50 \div 5 =$	98 $14 \div 2 =$
24 $30 \div 6 =$	49 $42 \div 6 =$	74 $18 \div 9 =$	99 $18 \div 6 =$
25 $18 \div 3 =$	50 $72 \div 9 =$	75 $20 \div 2 =$	100 $49 \div 7 =$

Time?	Time?	Time?	Time?
How do you think you are doing?	How did you do?	Is this your best score?	Which facts do you find the easiest?

Exercise 53A	Exercise 53B	Exercise 53C	Exercise 53D
Name:	Name:	Name:	Name:
Date:	Date:	Date:	Date:

1 $49 \div 7 =$	**26** $90 \div 10 =$	**51** $28 \div 7 =$	**76** $21 \div 7 =$
2 $36 \div 4 =$	**27** $21 \div 7 =$	**52** $50 \div 10 =$	**77** $10 \div 1 =$
3 $28 \div 7 =$	**28** $54 \div 9 =$	**53** $24 \div 6 =$	**78** $24 \div 4 =$
4 $30 \div 6 =$	**29** $12 \div 3 =$	**54** $42 \div 6 =$	**79** $27 \div 3 =$
5 $27 \div 9 =$	**30** $36 \div 6 =$	**55** $27 \div 9 =$	**80** $35 \div 5 =$
6 $10 \div 1 =$	**31** $20 \div 10 =$	**56** $21 \div 7 =$	**81** $18 \div 9 =$
7 $14 \div 7 =$	**32** $42 \div 7 =$	**57** $20 \div 4 =$	**82** $28 \div 7 =$
8 $35 \div 5 =$	**33** $6 \div 3 =$	**58** $6 \div 3 =$	**83** $20 \div 4 =$
9 $36 \div 6 =$	**34** $30 \div 6 =$	**59** $14 \div 7 =$	**84** $64 \div 8 =$
10 $27 \div 3 =$	**35** $49 \div 7 =$	**60** $45 \div 5 =$	**85** $14 \div 7 =$
11 $12 \div 3 =$	**36** $32 \div 4 =$	**61** $36 \div 6 =$	**86** $12 \div 3 =$
12 $35 \div 7 =$	**37** $7 \div 1 =$	**62** $42 \div 7 =$	**87** $48 \div 6 =$
13 $20 \div 4 =$	**38** $18 \div 6 =$	**63** $4 \div 2 =$	**88** $56 \div 7 =$
14 $72 \div 9 =$	**39** $56 \div 7 =$	**64** $9 \div 9 =$	**89** $80 \div 10 =$
15 $14 \div 2 =$	**40** $18 \div 2 =$	**65** $16 \div 4 =$	**90** $30 \div 6 =$
16 $18 \div 6 =$	**41** $27 \div 3 =$	**66** $35 \div 7 =$	**91** $42 \div 7 =$
17 $21 \div 7 =$	**42** $28 \div 7 =$	**67** $6 \div 1 =$	**92** $2 \div 1 =$
18 $18 \div 9 =$	**43** $24 \div 3 =$	**68** $15 \div 3 =$	**93** $72 \div 9 =$
19 $50 \div 5 =$	**44** $9 \div 1 =$	**69** $49 \div 7 =$	**94** $42 \div 6 =$
20 $42 \div 7 =$	**45** $42 \div 6 =$	**70** $27 \div 9 =$	**95** $40 \div 5 =$
21 $48 \div 6 =$	**46** $14 \div 7 =$	**71** $18 \div 6 =$	**96** $49 \div 7 =$
22 $18 \div 3 =$	**47** $32 \div 4 =$	**72** $10 \div 1 =$	**97** $16 \div 2 =$
23 $20 \div 4 =$	**48** $90 \div 9 =$	**73** $56 \div 7 =$	**98** $24 \div 4 =$
24 $56 \div 7 =$	**49** $35 \div 7 =$	**74** $24 \div 4 =$	**99** $35 \div 7 =$
25 $81 \div 9 =$	**50** $49 \div 7 =$	**75** $42 \div 6 =$	**100** $56 \div 7 =$

Time?	Time?	Time?	Time?
Try to concentrate even more!	How do you think you are doing?	What have you learnt today?	How could you recall these facts even quicker

Exercise 54A	Exercise 54B	Exercise 54C	Exercise 54D
Name:	Name:	Name:	Name:
Date:	Date:	Date:	Date:

1 $72 \div 8 =$	26 $15 \div 3 =$	51 $24 \div 8 =$	76 $56 \div 8 =$
2 $80 \div 10 =$	27 $16 \div 8 =$	52 $28 \div 7 =$	77 $28 \div 7 =$
3 $24 \div 8 =$	28 $6 \div 1 =$	53 $90 \div 10 =$	78 $16 \div 8 =$
4 $30 \div 6 =$	29 $35 \div 7 =$	54 $72 \div 8 =$	79 $24 \div 3 =$
5 $42 \div 7 =$	30 $16 \div 4 =$	55 $21 \div 7 =$	80 $9 \div 1 =$
6 $2 \div 1 =$	31 $9 \div 9 =$	56 $54 \div 9 =$	81 $42 \div 6 =$
7 $72 \div 9 =$	32 $24 \div 8 =$	57 $16 \div 8 =$	82 $14 \div 7 =$
8 $48 \div 8 =$	33 $4 \div 2 =$	58 $12 \div 3 =$	83 $32 \div 4 =$
9 $42 \div 6 =$	34 $42 \div 7 =$	59 $56 \div 8 =$	84 $90 \div 9 =$
10 $40 \div 5 =$	35 $72 \div 8 =$	60 $36 \div 6 =$	85 $24 \div 8 =$
11 $49 \div 7 =$	36 $36 \div 6 =$	61 $20 \div 10 =$	86 $35 \div 5 =$
12 $16 \div 8 =$	37 $45 \div 5 =$	62 $48 \div 8 =$	87 $20 \div 4 =$
13 $16 \div 2 =$	38 $48 \div 8 =$	63 $42 \div 7 =$	88 $18 \div 3 =$
14 $24 \div 4 =$	39 $14 \div 7 =$	64 $6 \div 3 =$	89 $48 \div 6 =$
15 $32 \div 8 =$	40 $6 \div 3 =$	65 $30 \div 6 =$	90 $42 \div 7 =$
16 $35 \div 7 =$	41 $20 \div 4 =$	66 $40 \div 8 =$	91 $50 \div 5 =$
17 $24 \div 4 =$	42 $32 \div 8 =$	67 $49 \div 7 =$	92 $72 \div 8 =$
18 $56 \div 7 =$	43 $21 \div 7 =$	68 $32 \div 4 =$	93 $18 \div 9 =$
19 $56 \div 8 =$	44 $27 \div 9 =$	69 $7 \div 1 =$	94 $21 \div 7 =$
20 $10 \div 1 =$	45 $40 \div 8 =$	70 $32 \div 8 =$	95 $18 \div 6 =$
21 $18 \div 6 =$	46 $42 \div 6 =$	71 $18 \div 6 =$	96 $48 \div 8 =$
22 $40 \div 8 =$	47 $24 \div 6 =$	72 $56 \div 7 =$	97 $14 \div 2 =$
23 $27 \div 9 =$	48 $50 \div 10 =$	73 $18 \div 2 =$	98 $72 \div 9 =$
24 $49 \div 7 =$	49 $56 \div 8 =$	74 $27 \div 3 =$	99 $20 \div 4 =$
25 $81 \div 9 =$	50 $12 \div 3 =$	75 $48 \div 8 =$	100 $100 \div 10 =$

Time?	Time?	Time?	Time?
Are the facts at your fingertips?	Try to really focus!	Which facts do you find the easiest?	Did you do well?

Exercise 55A	Exercise 55B	Exercise 55C	Exercise 55D
Name:	Name:	Name:	Name:
Date:	Date:	Date:	Date:

1 $6 \times 1 =$	**26** $20 \div 10 =$	**51** $20 \div 10 =$	**76** $1 \div 1 =$
2 $20 \div 10 =$	**27** $40 \div 10 =$	**52** $14 \div 2 =$	**77** $0 \times 9 =$
3 $3 \times 10 =$	**28** $10 \times 6 =$	**53** $8 \times 10 =$	**78** $40 \div 10 =$
4 $7 \div 1 =$	**29** $1 \times 6 =$	**54** $0 \times 10 =$	**79** $5 \div 1 =$
5 $0 \times 7 =$	**30** $10 \div 1 =$	**55** $9 \div 1 =$	**80** $1 \times 10 =$
6 $18 \div 2 =$	**31** $4 \times 10 =$	**56** $10 \times 10 =$	**81** $50 \div 10 =$
7 $10 \div 10 =$	**32** $2 \div 2 =$	**57** $100 \div 10 =$	**82** $6 \times 10 =$
8 $1 \times 10 =$	**33** $1 \times 9 =$	**58** $1 \times 2 =$	**83** $20 \div 2 =$
9 $5 \times 10 =$	**34** $7 \div 1 =$	**59** $8 \div 2 =$	**84** $0 \times 2 =$
10 $1 \times 4 =$	**35** $30 \div 10 =$	**60** $3 \div 1 =$	**85** $6 \div 1 =$
11 $0 \times 6 =$	**36** $0 \times 5 =$	**61** $1 \times 7 =$	**86** $50 \div 10 =$
12 $4 \div 1 =$	**37** $2 \div 1 =$	**62** $10 \div 10 =$	**87** $1 \times 1 =$
13 $3 \times 10 =$	**38** $5 \times 10 =$	**63** $1 \times 10 =$	**88** $5 \times 10 =$
14 $10 \div 2 =$	**39** $16 \div 2 =$	**64** $16 \div 2 =$	**89** $10 \div 1 =$
15 $1 \times 5 =$	**40** $0 \times 10 =$	**65** $1 \times 4 =$	**90** $1 \times 4 =$
16 $80 \div 10 =$	**41** $4 \div 1 =$	**66** $7 \div 1 =$	**91** $2 \div 2 =$
17 $9 \div 1 =$	**42** $60 \div 10 =$	**67** $90 \div 10 =$	**92** $0 \times 4 =$
18 $0 \times 8 =$	**43** $10 \times 10 =$	**68** $0 \times 6 =$	**93** $80 \div 10 =$
19 $9 \times 10 =$	**44** $1 \times 8 =$	**69** $1 \times 10 =$	**94** $14 \div 2 =$
20 $1 \times 4 =$	**45** $9 \times 1 =$	**70** $1 \div 2 =$	**95** $4 \times 10 =$
21 $18 \div 2 =$	**46** $4 \div 2 =$	**71** $0 \times 3 =$	**96** $1 \times 3 =$
22 $1 \times 5 =$	**47** $9 \times 10 =$	**72** $4 \times 10 =$	**97** $4 \div 1 =$
23 $2 \div 1 =$	**48** $5 \div 1 =$	**73** $8 \div 2 =$	**98** $1 \times 6 =$
24 $7 \times 10 =$	**49** $0 \times 1 =$	**74** $10 \times 7 =$	**99** $10 \div 2 =$
25 $2 \times 6 =$	**50** $10 \times 3 =$	**75** $2 \times 8 =$	**100** $7 \times 10 =$

Time?	Time?	Time?	Time?

Which facts did you find the hardest?

Did you beat your target?

Can you try to be faster?

Where do you need to improve?

Exercise 56A	Exercise 56B	Exercise 56C	Exercise 56D
Name:	Name:	Name:	Name:
Date:	Date:	Date:	Date:

1 $4 \times 10 =$	**26** $10 \div 2 =$	**51** $40 \div 5 =$	**76** $30 \div 10 =$
2 $15 \div 5 =$	**27** $80 \div 10 =$	**52** $2 \div 1 =$	**77** $2 \times 2 =$
3 $0 \times 9 =$	**28** $0 \times 6 =$	**53** $0 \times 4 =$	**78** $10 \div 5 =$
4 $14 \div 2 =$	**29** $1 \times 10 =$	**54** $4 \times 5 =$	**79** $7 \div 1 =$
5 $1 \times 5 =$	**30** $15 \div 5 =$	**55** $45 \div 5 =$	**80** $4 \times 10 =$
6 $2 \div 1 =$	**31** $5 \times 6 =$	**56** $4 \times 10 =$	**81** $2 \div 2 =$
7 $20 \div 10 =$	**32** $9 \div 1 =$	**57** $80 \div 8 =$	**82** $1 \times 9 =$
8 $2 \times 6 =$	**33** $2 \times 9 =$	**58** $2 \times 8 =$	**83** $40 \div 10 =$
9 $4 \times 5 =$	**34** $18 \div 2 =$	**59** $4 \div 1 =$	**84** $5 \times 6 =$
10 $1 \times 4 =$	**35** $30 \div 5 =$	**60** $14 \div 2 =$	**85** $20 \div 5 =$
11 $8 \times 10 =$	**36** $5 \times 9 =$	**61** $1 \times 3 =$	**86** $3 \div 1 =$
12 $7 \div 1 =$	**37** $2 \div 1 =$	**62** $70 \div 10 =$	**87** $0 \times 5 =$
13 $2 \times 3 =$	**38** $1 \times 6 =$	**63** $5 \times 8 =$	**88** $2 \times 8 =$
14 $45 \div 5 =$	**39** $20 \div 10 =$	**64** $15 \div 5 =$	**89** $10 \div 5 =$
15 $5 \times 8 =$	**40** $7 \times 10 =$	**65** $1 \times 4 =$	**90** $2 \times 10 =$
16 $18 \div 2 =$	**41** $50 \div 5 =$	**66** $1 \div 1 =$	**91** $8 \div 2 =$
17 $10 \div 10 =$	**42** $20 \div 5 =$	**67** $4 \div 2 =$	**92** $5 \times 5 =$
18 $0 \times 6 =$	**43** $5 \times 7 =$	**68** $6 \times 10 =$	**93** $100 \div 10 =$
19 $0 \times 8 =$	**44** $7 \times 10 =$	**69** $2 \times 5 =$	**94** $20 \div 10 =$
20 $2 \times 4 =$	**45** $5 \times 5 =$	**70** $3 \times 5 =$	**95** $0 \times 7 =$
21 $5 \div 5 =$	**46** $70 \div 10 =$	**71** $2 \times 7 =$	**96** $1 \times 3 =$
22 $5 \times 5 =$	**47** $1 \times 1 =$	**72** $6 \times 10 =$	**97** $9 \div 1 =$
23 $4 \div 1 =$	**48** $16 \div 2 =$	**73** $40 \div 5 =$	**98** $5 \times 5 =$
24 $2 \times 10 =$	**49** $2 \times 9 =$	**74** $5 \times 7 =$	**99** $40 \div 5 =$
25 $5 \times 3 =$	**50** $0 \times 4 =$	**75** $10 \times 10 =$	**100** $7 \times 5 =$

Exercise 56A	Exercise 56B	Exercise 56C	Exercise 56D
Time?	Time?	Time?	Time?

Is this your best score?

Have you reached your target?

Did you do well?

Do you think you are improving?

Exercise 57A	Exercise 57B	Exercise 57C	Exercise 57D
Name:	Name:	Name:	Name:
Date:	Date:	Date:	Date:

1 $3 \times 3 =$	**26** $10 \div 5 =$	**51** $14 \div 2 =$	**76** $15 \div 5 =$
2 $45 \div 5 =$	**27** $7 \div 1 =$	**52** $49 \div 7 =$	**77** $7 \times 10 =$
3 $4 \times 5 =$	**28** $6 \times 6 =$	**53** $2 \times 3 =$	**78** $100 \div 10 =$
4 $50 \div 10 =$	**29** $9 \times 5 =$	**54** $4 \times 5 =$	**79** $9 \div 1 =$
5 $6 \times 2 =$	**30** $16 \div 2 =$	**55** $7 \div 1 =$	**80** $7 \times 7 =$
6 $6 \div 1 =$	**31** $7 \times 10 =$	**56** $1 \times 8 =$	**81** $18 \div 2 =$
7 $16 \div 4 =$	**32** $9 \div 3 =$	**57** $9 \div 3 =$	**82** $1 \times 6 =$
8 $7 \times 7 =$	**33** $5 \times 5 =$	**58** $10 \times 10 =$	**83** $30 \div 5 =$
9 $1 \times 5 =$	**34** $10 \div 10 =$	**59** $45 \div 5 =$	**84** $2 \times 2 =$
10 $4 \times 4 =$	**35** $20 \div 5 =$	**60** $18 \div 2 =$	**85** $64 \div 8 =$
11 $0 \times 9 =$	**36** $1 \times 7 =$	**61** $2 \times 9 =$	**86** $2 \div 1 =$
12 $50 \div 10 =$	**37** $1 \div 1 =$	**62** $10 \div 10 =$	**87** $5 \times 9 =$
13 $3 \times 5 =$	**38** $2 \times 9 =$	**63** $5 \times 5 =$	**88** $4 \times 4 =$
14 $10 \div 1 =$	**39** $40 \div 5 =$	**64** $16 \div 4 =$	**89** $20 \div 10 =$
15 $2 \times 2 =$	**40** $0 \times 5 =$	**65** $8 \times 10 =$	**90** $2 \times 9 =$
16 $35 \div 5 =$	**41** $70 \div 10 =$	**66** $4 \div 1 =$	**91** $50 \div 5 =$
17 $2 \div 2 =$	**42** $20 \div 5 =$	**67** $10 \div 2 =$	**92** $1 \times 1 =$
18 $4 \times 10 =$	**43** $2 \times 8 =$	**68** $5 \times 7 =$	**93** $30 \div 10 =$
19 $2 \times 6 =$	**44** $9 \times 9 =$	**69** $2 \times 2 =$	**94** $2 \div 1 =$
20 $1 \times 1 =$	**45** $5 \times 8 =$	**70** $0 \times 10 =$	**95** $5 \times 6 =$
21 $64 \div 8 =$	**46** $9 \div 1 =$	**71** $6 \times 6 =$	**96** $6 \times 6 =$
22 $8 \times 8 =$	**47** $5 \times 10 =$	**72** $1 \times 2 =$	**97** $25 \div 5 =$
23 $80 \div 10 =$	**48** $40 \div 5 =$	**73** $80 \times 10 =$	**98** $1 \times 10 =$
24 $7 \times 10 =$	**49** $1 \times 1 =$	**74** $3 \times 5 =$	**99** $40 \div 5 =$
25 $10 \times 7 =$	**50** $4 \times 2 =$	**75** $8 \times 8 =$	**100** $7 \times 5 =$

Time?	Time?	Time?	Time?

Which facts did you find the hardest?

Did you beat your target?

Can you try to be faster?

Where do you need to improve?

Exercise 58A	**Exercise 58B**	**Exercise 58C**	**Exercise 58D**
Name:	Name:	Name:	Name:
Date:	Date:	Date:	Date:
1. 8 x 8 =	26. 7 ÷ 1 =	51. 81 ÷ 9 =	76. 18 ÷ 2 =
2. 16 ÷ 4 =	27. 16 ÷ 2 =	52. 50 ÷ 10 =	77. 7 x 9 =
3. 2 x 6 =	28. 3 x 3 =	53. 2 x 3 =	78. 10 ÷ 10 =
4. 50 ÷ 10 =	29. 1 x 4 =	54. 6 x 9 =	79. 16 ÷ 4 =
5. 4 x 10 =	30. 81 ÷ 9 =	55. 45 ÷ 5 =	80. 2 x 2 =
6. 27 ÷ 9 =	31. 8 x 10 =	56. 1 x 1 =	81. 10 ÷ 2 =
7. 10 ÷ 1 =	32. 9 ÷ 3 =	57. 4 ÷ 2 =	82. 5 x 7 =
8. 2 x 2 =	33. 8 x 9 =	58. 5 x 10 =	83. 80 ÷ 10 =
9. 3 x 9 =	34. 10 ÷ 10 =	59. 15 ÷ 5 =	84. 9 x 9 =
10. 5 x 5 =	35. 20 ÷ 5 =	60. 50 ÷ 5 =	85. 15 ÷ 5 =
11. 0 x 9 =	36. 9 x 9 =	61. 5 x 8 =	86. 100 ÷ 10 =
12. 35 ÷ 5 =	37. 9 ÷ 3 =	62. 14 ÷ 2 =	87. 1 x 8 =
13. 3 x 5 =	38. 3 x 5 =	63. 9 x 9 =	88. 3 x 9 =
14. 2 ÷ 2 =	39. 27 ÷ 9 =	64. 20 ÷ 10 =	89. 63 ÷ 9 =
15. 4 x 4 =	40. 1 x 2 =	65. 7 x 9 =	90. 6 x 10 =
16. 54 ÷ 9 =	41. 25 ÷ 5 =	66. 7 ÷ 1 =	91. 9 ÷ 1 =
17. 64 ÷ 8 =	42. 60 ÷ 10 =	67. 9 ÷ 3 =	92. 8 x 8 =
18. 1 x 5 =	43. 6 x 6 =	68. 2 x 8 =	93. 60 ÷ 10 =
19. 7 x 7 =	44. 4 x 9 =	69. 0 x 5 =	94. 2 ÷ 2 =
20. 6 x 2 =	45. 1 x 8 =	70. 3 x 3 =	95. 2 x 7 =
21. 80 ÷ 10 =	46. 5 ÷ 5 =	71. 5 x 6 =	96. 3 x 5 =
22. 6 x 9 =	47. 4 x 4 =	72. 10 x 10 =	97. 70 ÷ 10 =
23. 10 ÷ 5 =	48. 9 ÷ 1 =	73. 45 ÷ 9 =	98. 2 x 2 =
24. 4 x 5 =	49. 4 x 5 =	74. 3 x 3 =	99. 18 ÷ 9 =
25. 5 x 9 =	50. 6 x 6 =	75. 0 x 6 =	100. 9 x 9 =
Time?	Time?	Time?	Time?
Is this your best score?	Have you hit your target?	Did you do well?	Do you think you are improving?

Exercise 59A	Exercise 59B	Exercise 59C	Exercise 59D
Name:	Name:	Name:	Name:
Date:	Date:	Date:	Date:

#	59A	#	59B	#	59C	#	59D
1	$0 \times 9 =$	26	$9 \div 3 =$	51	$9 \div 1 =$	76	$15 \div 3 =$
2	$81 \div 9 =$	27	$25 \div 5 =$	52	$32 \div 4 =$	77	$4 \times 6 =$
3	$3 \times 5 =$	28	$1 \times 4 =$	53	$5 \times 9 =$	78	$27 \div 9 =$
4	$24 \div 4 =$	29	$10 \times 8 =$	54	$4 \times 8 =$	79	$10 \div 1 =$
5	$4 \times 3 =$	30	$50 \div 10 =$	55	$90 \div 9 =$	80	$3 \times 3 =$
6	$21 \div 3 =$	31	$4 \times 9 =$	56	$7 \times 10 =$	81	$24 \div 4 =$
7	$18 \div 2 =$	32	$36 \div 4 =$	57	$50 \div 10 =$	82	$1 \times 4 =$
8	$4 \times 4 =$	33	$3 \times 8 =$	58	$3 \times 6 =$	83	$27 \div 3 =$
9	$1 \times 5 =$	34	$27 \div 9 =$	59	$27 \div 9 =$	84	$4 \times 9 =$
10	$4 \times 8 =$	35	$10 \div 1 =$	60	$20 \div 4 =$	85	$35 \div 5 =$
11	$3 \times 5 =$	36	$8 \times 9 =$	61	$5 \times 5 =$	86	$18 \div 9 =$
12	$14 \div 2 =$	37	$35 \div 5 =$	62	$6 \div 3 =$	87	$5 \times 4 =$
13	$7 \times 7 =$	38	$2 \times 1 =$	63	$4 \times 9 =$	88	$2 \times 3 =$
14	$16 \div 4 =$	39	$12 \div 3 =$	64	$45 \div 5 =$	89	$20 \div 4 =$
15	$6 \times 2 =$	40	$3 \times 8 =$	65	$3 \times 5 =$	90	$6 \times 9 =$
16	$15 \div 3 =$	41	$20 \div 4 =$	66	$4 \div 2 =$	91	$64 \div 8 =$
17	$40 \div 5 =$	42	$72 \div 9 =$	67	$9 \div 9 =$	92	$4 \times 6 =$
18	$4 \times 7 =$	43	$8 \times 8 =$	68	$8 \times 9 =$	93	$12 \div 3 =$
19	$6 \times 9 =$	44	$7 \times 9 =$	69	$6 \times 10 =$	94	$80 \div 10 =$
20	$3 \times 4 =$	45	$3 \times 4 =$	70	$4 \times 7 =$	95	$1 \times 1 =$
21	$32 \div 4 =$	46	$14 \div 2 =$	71	$3 \times 7 =$	96	$5 \times 10 =$
22	$4 \times 5 =$	47	$7 \times 10 =$	72	$7 \times 7 =$	97	$72 \div 9 =$
23	$9 \div 9 =$	48	$64 \div 8 =$	73	$16 \div 4 =$	98	$3 \times 6 =$
24	$3 \times 9 =$	49	$6 \times 6 =$	74	$3 \times 9 =$	99	$16 \div 2 =$
25	$4 \times 6 =$	50	$7 \times 9 =$	75	$4 \times 3 =$	100	$6 \times 8 =$

Time?	Time?	Time?	Time?
Did you beat your score?	Which facts do you find the hardest?	Is this your best score?	Try to concentrate even more?

Exercise 60A	Exercise 60B	Exercise 60C	Exercise 60D
Name:	Name:	Name:	Name:
Date:	Date:	Date:	Date:

1 $6 \times 9 =$	**26** $42 \div 7 =$	**51** $9 \div 9 =$	**76** $32 \div 8 =$
2 $9 \div 10 =$	**27** $6 \div 3 =$	**52** $24 \div 8 =$	**77** $4 \times 8 =$
3 $3 \times 4 =$	**28** $3 \times 5 =$	**53** $4 \times 6 =$	**78** $21 \div 7 =$
4 $72 \div 8 =$	**29** $3 \times 4 =$	**54** $1 \times 1 =$	**79** $27 \div 9 =$
5 $4 \times 6 =$	**30** $30 \div 6 =$	**55** $4 \div 2 =$	**80** $5 \times 8 =$
6 $21 \div 7 =$	**31** $6 \times 7 =$	**56** $10 \times 5 =$	**81** $40 \div 8 =$
7 $54 \div 9 =$	**32** $40 \div 8 =$	**57** $42 \div 7 =$	**82** $9 \times 9 =$
8 $9 \times 7 =$	**33** $1 \times 8 =$	**58** $4 \times 8 =$	**83** $42 \div 6 =$
9 $6 \times 9 =$	**34** $49 \div 7 =$	**59** $72 \div 8 =$	**84** $8 \times 2 =$
10 $8 \times 10 =$	**35** $32 \div 4 =$	**60** $36 \div 6 =$	**85** $24 \div 6 =$
11 $8 \times 7 =$	**36** $4 \times 4 =$	**61** $0 \times 6 =$	**86** $50 \div 10 =$
12 $16 \div 8 =$	**37** $7 \div 1 =$	**62** $45 \div 5 =$	**87** $7 \times 9 =$
13 $5 \times 5 =$	**38** $3 \times 8 =$	**63** $7 \times 8 =$	**88** $3 \times 7 =$
14 $12 \div 3 =$	**39** $32 \div 8 =$	**64** $48 \div 8 =$	**89** $56 \div 8 =$
15 $1 \times 8 =$	**40** $4 \times 9 =$	**65** $3 \times 6 =$	**90** $3 \times 3 =$
16 $56 \div 8 =$	**41** $18 \div 6 =$	**66** $14 \div 7 =$	**91** $49 \div 7 =$
17 $36 \div 6 =$	**42** $56 \div 7 =$	**67** $6 \div 3 =$	**92** $9 \times 9 =$
18 $3 \times 6 =$	**43** $5 \times 4 =$	**68** $5 \times 8 =$	**93** $27 \div 9 =$
19 $6 \times 7 =$	**44** $4 \times 7 =$	**69** $4 \times 6 =$	**94** $40 \div 8 =$
20 $9 \times 2 =$	**45** $2 \times 3 =$	**70** $1 \times 1 =$	**95** $7 \times 8 =$
21 $20 \times 10 =$	**46** $18 \div 2 =$	**71** $7 \times 9 =$	**96** $4 \times 7 =$
22 $10 \times 10 =$	**47** $6 \times 8 =$	**72** $5 \times 10 =$	**97** $18 \div 6 =$
23 $48 \div 8 =$	**48** $27 \div 3 =$	**73** $20 \div 4 =$	**98** $5 \times 8 =$
24 $3 \times 9 =$	**49** $7 \times 7 =$	**74** $3 \times 6 =$	**99** $10 \div 1 =$
25 $8 \times 7 =$	**50** $9 \times 4 =$	**75** $8 \times 8 =$	**100** $2 \times 3 =$

Time?	Time? –	Time?	Time?

Is this your best score yet? Did you beat your target? Have you reached your target yet? How do you think you are doing?

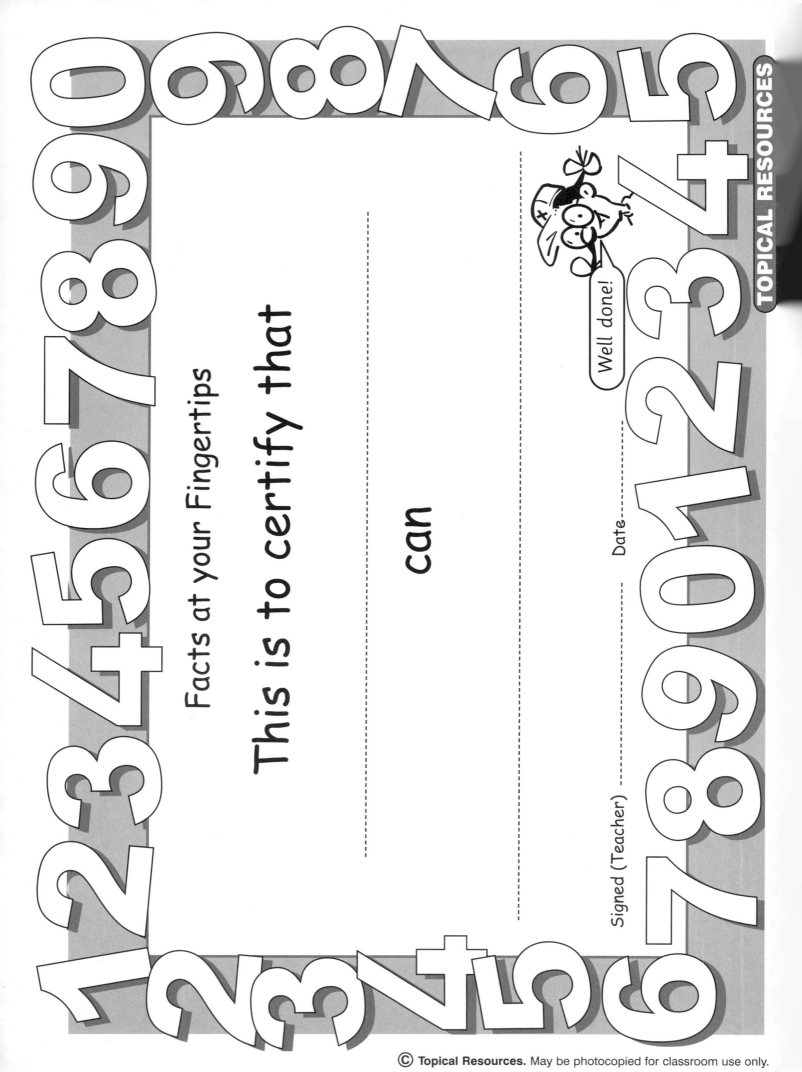

Facts at your Fingertips

This is to certify that

can

Well done!

Date

Signed (Teacher)